Portuguese Fairy Tales

Folk and fairy tales are the product of mountain and forest. Lusitania, as Portugal was called in far-off days, had plenty of both. There were dragons and a variety of enchanted and supernatural beings living there, both on land and in the sea, but scarcely any ogres – or rather Lusitania had its own special kind, the Moor.

After the Arab conquest of much of the Iberian peninsula, the dark-skinned invader with his different faith and different ways became the embodiment of all evil to the simple country people, and quite put the ogre out of business, taking his place in folk tales. That explains why, between these covers, there are more Moors than dragons, and not a single ogre.

Portuguese Fairy Tales

Retold by

MAURICE AND PAMELA MICHAEL

Illustrated by

HARRY AND ILSE TOOTHILL

FREDERICK MULLER LIMITED

First published in Great Britain in 1965
by Frederick Muller Limited, 110 Fleet Street, London, E.C.4

Reprinted 1967

Printed and bound by
Cox & Wyman, Ltd., London Fakenham and Reading

Contents

Illustrations

ONE

The Black Spider

ONCE LONG, LONG AGO, the son of a king of Egypt came to the ancient land of Lusitania and there built himself a mansion. He had many servants and men-at-arms and a sorcerer who was able to cast the most powerful spells. What happened then nobody knows. The king's son may have sold his estates and returned to Egypt, or perhaps he was driven out; but years later, at the time of this story, the mansion and surrounding lands were owned by a noble lord who had a lovely daughter of whose beauty he was immensely proud.

One day the young son of a noble family, a poor knight with only a very plain suit of mail, but a heart of gold, came riding past. He had noticed how the bare and rather sterile country had been made to grow good crops, and now he reached a long high wall above which he could just glimpse the tiled roofs of several buildings. He followed this wall for a long way, before arriving at a gateway. One of the great gates stood open and the young knight rode through, because he wanted to water his horse and because his own throat was parched by the heat of the day.

Inside, the young man found himself in a great courtyard, in the middle of which was a lake with a fountain playing, surrounded by shady trees and beds with roses and other flowers. To his surprise the clatter of hooves brought no servants scurrying, so the knight dismounted, removed his helmet and in his dusty armour strode across to where he could see someone sitting. As he drew near he saw that the figure was that of a young girl. She was richly dressed and so lovely it quite took his breath away. The girl looked up as he approached, and as she saw the brown hair and handsome features of the young knight, his winning smile and the admiration in his eyes, her heart leaped. The young knight saluted her and said:

'May a traveller ask for water for his horse and a drink for himself from one so lovely and obviously so rich?'

The girl clapped her hands and called: 'Marta!' and a few moments later a young negress appeared, whom the girl ordered to bring a drink for the young knight and to tell one of the stable-lads to bring water for his horse.

While they waited, the two stood looking at each other. The knight asked: 'Who are you?'

'I am Neiva and my father is lord of these estates.'

'Why then are you not happy? I would be happy if I lived in such a place and my father owned all this,' said the young knight, waving his arm in sweeping gesture to embrace the house and the garden with all their signs of wealth and prosperity. 'But you look sad.'

'I am sad,' said the girl, 'but not, of course, all the time. The thing is that my father thinks that no one, who is not richer than he, braver than he, nobler than he and handsomer than he is good enough for his daughter. As a result, all who come to ask for my hand are dismissed contemptuously and I am afraid that I shall die a spinster.'

'That would indeed be a pity,' said the young knight. 'I would gladly have a word with your father myself, but though I am of noble birth and brave, I am certainly not rich, let alone richer than he. In fact, my horse and my sword are about all I own.'

'That might be good enough for me, but certainly not for my father,' said the girl and smiled sadly.

By this time the young knight's horse had been watered and the girl told him that he must go, because her father was very jealous and there would be an awful fuss if he found her talking to a stranger. So, the young knight mounted and rode out through the gate and away.

After that, the young knight could think of nothing but the girl he had met in that lovely garden. Many days later, he was sitting in the public room of an inn away up in the mountains, alone with the innkeeper and his wife. They were a kindly couple and, after supper, they asked the young knight why he looked so sad. He told them that he had fallen in love with a girl whose father would only let her marry someone who was richer, nobler and braver than he, and that though he was just as noble, he was not rich, but poor.

'Perhaps,' said the innkeeper's wife, 'if you could prove that you were braver than he, he would not mind about you being poor, because it sounds as though he has enough for you as well as for himself.'

'Maybe,' said the young knight, 'but how can I prove to him that I am brave?'

'Just a moment,' said the innkeeper's wife. 'I have an idea.' So saying, she flung a shawl round her shoulders and hurried out.

It was a long time before the woman returned and,

when she did, she held a small box in her hand. Going to the young knight she gave him the box and said:

'Inside this box is a small black spider. The wise-woman who lives a little way up the mountainside has put a spell on it, so that the moment it gets out of the box and feels the heat of the sun, it will turn into an enormous dragon. If you could let it go in this man's garden and kill it, perhaps then he would think you good enough for his daughter.'

The young knight did not know how to thank her enough. Now at last he could hope and he was determined to try his luck. So the very next morning he saddled his horse and rode down into the valley again and back the way he had come.

Reaching the River Mondego, not far from where the girl lived, he halted. Taking off his armour he scrubbed and polished it with river sand till it was burnished and shone like silver. Then he groomed his horse, combed its tail with his fingers and made it shine and look as handsome as he. Then he mounted and rode on.

It was afternoon when he once more rode through the great gateway and again saw the girl and her black servant walking under the trees. This time, however, the sound of his horse's hooves brought servants scurrying, and the girl had no more than recognized the young knight with a gasp of surprise, when a footman came bustling up and asked him what he was doing and why he was there. The young knight answered that he had come to speak to the girl's father for he wished to ask for his daughter's hand in marriage. The footman marched away and returned a little later, telling the young knight to follow him.

Clutching his little box the young knight was ushered into a great hall, at one end of which stood a cluster of knights and courtiers. As the knight walked towards them, he saw in the middle a tall dark man with a terrifying scowl on his face, and the young knight's heart sank. Then the tall dark man asked him who he was that dared to come like this and ask for his daughter's hand. The young knight told him who his father was and his lineage, and the man's face became less angry. Then he asked what deeds of daring the young knight had performed, so the young knight had to say that he had been in this battle and that, yet so far he had not had an opportunity to distinguish himself. The tall man's face clouded and, when he asked what inheritance the young knight had, and the young knight confessed that he was the youngest of seven sons and would inherit nothing, the tall man's face was angrier than ever and he ordered the young knight to be gone. As he walked away the young knight passed an open window, and quickly opening his little box he shook the spider out into the courtyard.

Almost at once there was a scream and great bellow. Everyone rushed to look out and there, to their astonishment, they saw an enormous dragon with a scaly back and long neck and tail. It was twisting its ugly head from side to side and the talons of one of its great feet were fastened in poor Marta, the serving girl. The dragon was a fearsome-looking sight and involuntarily everyone took a step back.

Then the tall dark man turned to his courtiers and said:

'Someone go and deal with that.'

But no one moved. The knights just stood staring down at the ground or up into the air, as though they had not heard, which of course they had. Then Neiva's father turned to a burly man with great broad shoulders and a scarred cheek:

'Deal with this beast, Dom Carlos,' he said.

'My lord, I am too old for dragons,' said the burly man, eyes cast down.

'But I am not!' exclaimed the young knight. 'I will fight with this dragon.' Saying which, he drew his sword and ran down the stairs and out into the courtyard.

At the sound of the young knight's mailed feet ringing on the stones of the courtyard, the dragon turned its wicked head, its great tongue flickering and eyes glaring balefully. Seeing the young knight, it turned half round with surprising speed and lashed out with its tail, which the young knight just managed to avoid by leaping into the air. The tail had wicked-looking spikes along its top and was armoured with dull-grey scales. The force of it was such that it would have killed whoever it struck.

Again the tail lashed out and again the young knight leapt into the air, this time slashing at the tail with his sword as it passed under him, but he missed. A third time the dragon struck at him with its tail and this time the steel bit home. The dragon gave an angry grunt and its tail went limp. Then, turning round with the same amazing agility, the dragon came swiftly at the young knight, as though intending to crush him, leaving the body of young Marta lying lifeless on the ground.

Realizing that at all costs he must not let himself be driven against the wall, the young knight grasped his sword in both hands and charged at the dragon. The two met with a shock that could be heard above the scrape of mailed feet and horny talons. The young knight's sword entered the dragon's neck low down, where it joined the body, and as he wrenched it free a great spurt of blood gushed out. The dragon lurched

. . . grasped his sword in both hands.

forward, knocking the sword from the young knight's hand, but he just managed to jump clear, and, drawing the dagger that hung at his belt, he leaped astride the dragon's neck and plunged the blade into it again and again.

Briefly, the young knight was unseated by the convulsive movements of the dying dragon, but he jumped back on again. Finally the dragon lay stretched out motionless. The young knight stood up, and sheathing his dagger walked slowly and stiffly up the stairs and back into the great hall.

As he entered, Neiva's father came towards him, his face smiling and friendly.

'Young sir,' he said. 'You have put us all to shame. You may not have wealth, but you have more courage than any of us and if you wish the hand of my daughter, she shall be yours.'

Then Neiva appeared at her father's side, her face alight with happiness, and the young knight knelt before her and kissed her hand.

Years later, those who had attended the wedding banquet of the fair Neiva and her young knight, would tell how above the heads of bride and bridegroom there had hung a small black spider; while in a certain village up in the Estrella Mountains people still wondered how the wise-woman, who had always been so poor, had managed to conjure up such wealth in her little cottage on the mountainside that she had never had to tell fortunes or cast spells again.

TWO

The Child and the Fig

ONCE UPON A TIME there was a little girl who lived with her step-mother. Her real mother had died when she was a baby, and her father had married again. He was a rich merchant and had sailed away in one of his ships to trade for silks and spices in far-away India, but he had not been heard of for so many years that it was feared his ship must have been lost in a storm, or captured by pirates, and the little girl was very unhappy. She loved her father and missed him sadly, particularly as her step-mother was a strict, hard woman, who never showed any affection or kindness towards her poor little step-daughter; indeed, the only family love that the little girl knew was from her aunt, her dead mother's sister, who lived in the same town and had several jolly children who were sometimes allowed to visit and play with their cousin.

What the little girl did not know was that her step-mother was a magician, and at night people used to come secretly and tap on the door and give the girl's step-mother money so that she would make a charm or cast a spell for them. In this way the magician had become quite rich, but not any nicer or kinder. Now the house where this little girl and her step-mother lived had the most beautiful garden, and the step-mother was terribly proud of it. Most of her days were spent in cutting, planting and pruning things in her garden, or giving instructions to the gardener to dig, weed and water, and everyone thought how magical it was the way the garden bloomed. The children had to be very careful when they played in case they broke off the head of a flower or trod on some precious plant, for the step-mother would fly into the most dreadful rage if they did the least damage and would send the cousins scurrying home and keep her poor little step-daughter shut up as a punishment.

The garden was filled with the most beautiful flowers. Roses, lilies and camellias grew in abundance, and wistaria crept with its twisted grey stems over the white-washed walls of the garden and hung its sweet-scented tassels of lavender flowers so that the shadows of them melted and merged in a dapple of blue and lavender in the strong sunlight and the gentle breeze. There were pretty fountains splashing into cool, tiled pools with stone seats set beside them on which one could sit and rest in the heat of the day. Altogether the garden would have been the most delightful place in the world, if only its owner had been a little less strict and fussy and thought of it as a garden to enjoy rather than a place where one scarcely dared to tread.

In the centre of this lovely garden stood a huge, old fig-tree. In summer its wide, green branches spread a pool of dark shade and were laden with the most delicious fruit that hung like dark, glistening pearls among the leaves. One year this old tree produced a fig of unusual size and of the most perfect shape and colour. The girl's step-mother was so proud of this fig and so anxious that it should be perfectly ripe before it was picked, that she told her little step-daughter to watch over it, for she was afraid that the birds might steal it, or peck at it and spoil it, for everyone knows that a bird is as good a judge of ripe fruit as anybody. So proud was the woman of her fig that she threatened to kill the little girl if she was careless enough to let the birds steal it, and the poor child was terrified because she knew what her stepmother's rages were like. So she used to get up very early to keep watch by the fig-tree, armed with a long cane with which to scare away the birds, and would only leave it when darkness fell and the birds began to roost. But one day her attention was drawn by the old gardener who was killing a snake with a stick, and while she wasn't looking a specially bold bird swooped down and before she had time to frighten it off, it seized the fig in its beak and flew away. The little girl was horrified and ran to her step-mother sobbing, begging her forgiveness and describing how the bird must have been waiting for a chance to steal the fig when her back was turned. 'You naughty, wicked girl,' shrieked the woman. 'I will never forgive you for being so careless, but I will show you more mercy than you deserve. I shall not kill you, but I shall turn you into a rose bush and bind you with a magic spell which will never be broken until someone brings me a pearl as dark and beautiful as the fig that was stolen and hangs it from one of your branches.' Then the wicked woman began to mutter and whisper strange rhymes and verses until the little girl grew stiff with fright at the cold, angry gleam in her eyes; her arms turned into branches, her feet were rooted in the ground and where her bright golden hair had curled about her slim, childish shoulders, a shower of beautiful yellow roses crowned the little rose bush that now stood beneath the old fig-tree.

After some time had passed the little girl's aunt came

B

with her children to inquire if her niece was ill, as they had none of them seen her for so long. The wicked lady said that the little girl had run away from home and that she was such a bad, ungrateful child that she was glad to see the last of her. While they were talking some of the cousins wandered into the garden and were attracted by the beautiful new rose growing beneath the old fig-tree. So lovely were the yellow flowers, so perfect in shape, so sweetly scented and just the colour of sunlight, that one of them could not resist plucking just one. As she did so, she was frightened at hearing a soft voice from the rose saying :

> As a rose tree I must dwell
> Guarded by a wicked spell
> Nought can save me, but a pearl
> Can change me back into a girl.

The little cousin ran to her mother in fright and held the rose out to her, so that she too could hear the strange words. The wicked step-mother stamped with rage and shrieked to the child to give her the rose immediately, but the child's mother refused to do so and hurried away to the magistrate to prove that some dark deed had been performed on her poor little niece and to ask him to bring the wicked step-mother to justice. There was a strong feeling of hatred against witches and those who could work black magic in the town, and the magistrate sent soldiers to capture the evil woman and throw her into prison. But he could not change the rose tree back into a little girl. Every day her cousins and her aunt came to water the little tree and pull the weeds away from its roots, and it gave out a sweeter fragrance when their tears of pity fell on the ground and their loving fingers touched its bright blossoms.

One day the town was astir with excitement, for before dawn a great ship had sailed into port and it was said to be laden with treasure. The captain was none other than the little girl's long-lost father and he hurried through the streets to his own house eager to find his wife and child. Imagine his surprise and dismay when he found the house deserted, and in the garden, instead of the beautiful display of well-tended shrubs and flowers that he remembered, he found it all neglected and overgrown with weeds, except for one little rose which grew beneath the fig-tree where the ground had been carefully watered and weeded. Wearily the rich merchant reached out his hand to pluck one of the yellow roses, which were the only sign of beauty left in the garden, and as he did so the sad little voice whispered:

As a rose tree I must dwell
Guarded by a wicked spell.
Naught can save me, but a pearl
Can change me back into your girl.

It was the voice of his daughter! The poor man trembled with emotion and murmured, 'My darling child, I have brought many pearls and jewels as gifts for you, only tell me what I must do to break the spell so that I may hold you in my arms!'

Bring a pearl rare and fine
The colour must be dark as wine.
Hang it from a branch above,
And I'll reward you with my love.

The merchant drew from his bag an exquisite pear-shaped pearl which glowed with a dusky fire, and reaching up he hung it from one of the branches of the rose bush. All at once the rose bush was changed back into a beautiful little girl and she ran to her father and straight into his open arms. They wept for joy at having found each other again, and then she told him the story of the garden, the step-mother and her cruel spell. The merchant promised that he would never leave her again and would stay to love and care for her for the rest of his life. He had brought back great riches and treasure from his long, adventurous voyages, and now they would buy a new house with an even better garden. And this they did. It was a magnificent house and its garden was as beautiful and much more delightful than the other. The girl had many friends and gave lovely parties, and she and her father enjoyed each other's love and companionship for many years.

THREE

The Puss's Tail

ONCE A LONG TIME ago, when cats were treated as people just like us, one handsome young tom went into a barber's shop to have his whiskers trimmed. While snipping away, the barber noticed that puss had an exceptionally long fluffy tail; so, anxious for a little more money, he said:

'Look, sir. Your tail is a bit long to balance properly with your type of figure. If you were to have it shortened you would be much more handsome than you are now.'

The cat, being young and very vain, thought this sounded good advice and agreed that the barber should lop his tail. So the barber sharpened his razor and taking hold of the fluffy end, with one good slash cut off the best part of puss's tail. For this service he charged twice as much as for trimming the cat's whiskers, but the vain puss gladly paid what he asked.

Puss swaggered off, delighted to think that he was even better looking than before, but then a thought struck him: why should the barber keep his tail? He decided to go back and claim it. So he turned round, and running back to the barber's shop he demanded his tail. The barber, however, had already thrown the fluffy thing away along with the other sweepings from his floor, so he told the cat that he could not have it.

'Give me my tail, or I'll take one of your razors,' said the cat.

The barber, determined that he was not going to rummage in the dustbin for any puss's tail, refused; so the cat, jumping up, took one of the barber's razors and ran out of the shop.

Feeling very pleased with himself, puss walked on. Presently he came across a woman with a basket of fish and, seeing that she had no knife with which to gut and clean them, he felt suddenly sorry for her and said to her: 'Here, my good woman, take this razor. I don't need it. Use it to gut your fish.' The woman was very grateful and thanked the cat profusely, and puss walked on well pleased with himself for being so generous. Suddenly a thought struck him: the woman ought to have given him a fish in return for the razor! She was mean not to have thought of it, he decided, so puss turned and going back to the woman he demanded a fish. The woman refused to give him one, but the cat pounced on one and ran off with it.

Farther along the road, puss came to a mill. The miller was young and poor and he was sitting on a bench outside having his dinner, which consisted of dry bread. Puss thought it a shame that anyone should have to eat dry bread, and so gave the miller the fish to eat with his bread. He then walked on, telling himself what a kind, generous chap he was; but when he had gone a little way down the road, the cat regretted his generosity and decided he wanted the fish back for his own dinner. Running back to the mill, the cat said to the young miller: 'I want that fish back.'

But the hungry young miller had already eaten it and couldn't have given it back, even if he had been willing to. Hearing this, the cat said:

'Then I shall take a bag of your flour.' And pouncing, the cat seized a bag and ran off with it.

Farther down the road, puss came to a school. Seeing that the young mistress was thin and poor and then learning that she had nothing for dinner for her pupils, puss gave her the bag of flour to make gruel for herself and the children. Then off puss went, once more feeling what a good, generous fellow he was. But he had not gone very far when he again regretted his generosity and, running to the school, asked for the flour back. But the schoolmistress had already made the gruel and she and the children had eaten it all up, so there was nothing to give back. Puss was furious and said: 'All right, then, I'll take one of your girls instead.' And seizing one of the children, he ran off with her.

It was not long before puss got very tired of carrying the girl, so, coming to a laundry, he went in and offered the girl to the laundress, telling her that with the girl's help she would get her work done more quickly. The laundress, who was old and tired, was very grateful; and puss went on his way, delighted to be rid of the girl. Before long, however, he began to feel that he ought to have had something in return for his present, so, going back to the laundress, he demanded a shirt. The laundress was most indignant because, of course, the shirts were not hers; so she refused to give the cat one, but he just snatched one and ran off.

Feeling triumphant, the cat went on his way, the shirt tucked under his arm. Soon he became tired of carrying the shirt and wondered what he could do with it. Then, round the corner came a young musician, carrying a gleaming violin which was obviously his pride, but not his fortune, for he did not even have a shirt and the rest of his clothes were poor and shabby.

... offered the girl to the laundress.

'Here,' said the cat. 'I see you have no shirt, so put this one on.'

The musician took the shirt and put it on. He was delighted to find that it fitted perfectly. Then, turning round, he saw that the cat had taken his violin and was already half-way to the next corner. Now the young man was not really a good musician, and having lost his violin he had to take a job. Being able to read and write he got a job as clerk working for a rich merchant, and discovered that he had a head for business; in fact, he was so clever at it that before many years had passed he was richer than the merchant and had married a nobleman's daughter and lived with her in a large house in lovely gardens.

The puss, being hungry when he got to the next village, played the violin outside the inn there, and produced such a gay and merry tune that people poured money into puss's hat, when he took it round. Seeing that he had been so successful, puss practised hard and before long he was even giving concerts. He became a famous violinist and all the kings and princesses of the world invited him to come and play for them.

FOUR

The Invisible Hands

A CERTAIN YOUNG MAN once set out, like so many young men both before and since, to travel the world. Coming to a certain town in the fair land of Portugal, he found that he could not get a room. At every hostelry and inn to which he went he was told that they had no vacant room; in fact he was assured that the whole town was full and that there was not a bed to be had anywhere. Then it began to rain and the young man felt desperate. At the next inn the innkeeper suggested that, if a roof over his head was all he needed, he could go to a castle just outside the town and shelter there. The castle was empty but, said the innkeeper, haunted.

Apparently, the family to whom the castle had belonged for generations and generations had left quite suddenly, because of the awful noise that had kept them awake in their beds and the ghastly apparition that had taken to wandering through the rooms at night. Now the castle and its grounds had been abandoned and left to rack and ruin. The young man was not afraid of any ghost or apparition, so he went off at once, determined to spend the night in the haunted castle. When he reached it, however, and had walked up the overgrown drive to the dismal, decayed front where the main entrance was, a queer feeling came over him. One would not say that he was afraid, because he was a brave young man, but a little inner voice began telling him that the wide veranda would suit his purpose admirably and that there was no need to go inside. So, taking his cloak, he made himself a bed on the veranda floor and lay down just as night was falling.

He was lying awake wondering at the fate of the old castle and why it gave him this strange feeling, when he saw a hand that seemed to be holding a lighted candle out towards him. Then the hand beckoned. He waited. The hand beckoned again, so the young man got to his feet, and going to a french window he tried the catch. The window opened and the young man stepped inside.

He found himself in a magnificently furnished room in the middle of which stood a table laid with a place for one and all sorts of dishes piled with the most delicious food and a large number of bottles. The sight of all these good things reminded the young man that he was hungry, so, pulling up a chair, he sat down and began to eat. He had some pie, then some cold meat and salad, then some more pie, then some fruit, and he sampled three different bottles of wine. By the time he could eat no more, he was feeling quite drowsy and, resting his head on his hand, he fell asleep. While he slept, a gold ring that he wore was taken from his finger and another ring put in its place.

When the young man woke, as he soon did because his arm was numb, he again saw the hand beckoning. He got up and followed the beckoning hand, which led him to a room where he found a magnificent bed with the covers turned down and looking so inviting that, without a moment's hesitation, he slipped out of his clothes and dived in between the sheets. It was then that he noticed the new ring on his finger, but he was so

. . . he fell asleep.

sleepy that he did not have much time to wonder, but fell asleep again.

About midnight, the young man was awakened by someone moving in the room. Being a brave young man, he did not pull the bedclothes over his head, but called out asking who was there, whether it was a man or a woman. Then a faint voice replied:

'I am a girl, an unfortunate Moorish girl, and have been kept here under a spell for years and years. If you are really brave enough, you can free me; and if you do, I will make you richer than your wildest dreams. But I am afraid it won't be easy. You will have to stay here for three days and nights, during which time all sorts of invisible beings will try to frighten you away. They will even wound you; but if you stay, you will find under your bed three bottles, one drop from each of which will heal all your wounds. Oh, please will you try? If you do, I will give you three bags of gold and you will be able to spend as much money as you like. If the bags are empty, you will only have to say: "Oh, what a pity, I have no money!" and at once the bags will be full again. Will you try?' Before the young man had time to answer, the girl went away, for though he had not seen her, he could sense that she was no longer there; but he decided to stay in the castle and break the spell. Quite apart from the money, which would be most welcome, he wanted to rescue someone who, if she was as pretty as her voice, must be very good-looking indeed.

Turning over on his side, the young man thought he would try to go to sleep again, but invisible hands laid hold of him and rolled him out of bed, and when he crawled back again, they pulled him off by his feet and then began beating and pommelling him all over, while other hands clutched at his throat or jabbed a knife into him. Whenever he jumped to his feet, he was tripped up and once he received such a blow on the chin that he saw stars. The worst thing was that he could not fight back. When he hit out, his fists struck nothing but the empty air, when he tried to grasp a throttling hand, there was nothing there, but at once other hands were elsewhere about his body hitting, pulling, jabbing, scratching, while voices shrieked and bellowed at him in the most horrifying manner. When daylight came, the young man's clothes were torn and he was bleeding in several places, while one eye was closed and the teeth on one side of his jaw felt loose and sore; but his invisible adversaries had withdrawn as the first bird broke into song in the wilderness of a garden outside.

The young man felt sore and weak, and rather dizzy, but he managed to crawl to the bed, under which he found three small bottles. He poured a drop from each into a goblet of wine and drained it. At once he felt better and to his amazement he saw his wounds stop bleeding and heal. His black-eye was swollen no more and the rents in his clothes mended themselves. Then, going into the room where he had had that lovely supper, he found more food waiting and realized again that he was hungry.

After breakfast, the young man went exploring in the castle, but all its many rooms were empty and nowhere was there a sign of life or movement, not even in the rooms where he had slept and eaten. When he got back to them, the sun was pouring in and they too were empty, and the only sound was the dull echo of his own footsteps. But as soon as night fell, the beckoning hand returned and led the young man to another table covered with dishes from which came the most appetizing smells. This time there was chicken and duck, roast boar and fresh river trout; more and different wines, and strange fruit that the young man had never seen or eaten before. Then, as soon as he lay down in bed, the invisible hands returned and the young man had an even worse time of it than before. If he had not been proud as well as brave, he would probably have run from the castle, but he managed to hold out till the first bird-call from the garden made the invisible hands withdraw. Again the young man crawled to the bed and fished the three bottles out from under it, and again the three drops restored him in a truly miraculous way.

At the end of the third night, which was the worst of all, the young man found not only three bottles under the bed, but three bags full of heavy gold coins. Having restored himself with the magic drops, the young man went into the next room expecting to find breakfast waiting; but the room was bare. Turning back he saw that the bedroom, too, was bare, except for the three bags standing in the middle of the floor; so, pocketing the bags the young man left the castle and walked back into the town where he went to the best inn and had breakfast.

After breakfast, the young man thought he would test his bags of money. First, he bought himself some new clothes, then a horse and saddle and bridle; but still two of the bags were full, so seeing that a certain very elegant-looking house was for sale, he went and bought it. By the time he had completed the transaction, the last bag was empty and he did not even have enough to pay for his lunch. So, he said quietly to himself: 'Oh, what a pity! I have no money!' and at once he could feel the pockets in which he had put the bags being suddenly weighed down, and, pulling out the bags, he found them full again.

After that the young man rode through the country and in every village he either gave money to the poor, or bought a house for the old people, or provided food and clothing for the needy. Eventually he reached the land of the Moors, and being attracted by a large estate near the city where the viceroy lived, he bought it and settled down there to live. Of course everyone talked about the rich stranger and the magnificent way his house was being furnished, and news of him even reached the viceroy, who decided that he would send the rich foreigner an invitation to the breakfast which was to precede the wedding of his daughter, recently returned from a long absence.

The young man found himself seated near the viceroy's daughter. Suddenly he noticed that she was wearing a ring exactly like the one that had been taken from him in the haunted castle. Then he heard the princess speak and the voice was that of the girl who had pleaded with him to spend three nights in the castle and so release her from her spell. The young man could scarcely believe his eyes. Wishing to be sure, he tried to draw the girl's attention to his own hand on which he wore the ring put there in place of his own. Every time he reached out for a dish, he did so slowly and in such a way that the back of his hand was turned towards the girl. At the third attempt he saw the girl give a start and look across at him. Then, holding up her hand to ask for silence, the girl turned to her father and said:

'Father dear, before we go any further with the wedding ceremony there is a question I must ask, if our guests will allow me. I lost the key of my jewel chest and I had another made instead. Now, I have found the old one and would like you and our guests to tell me which I ought to use?'

'My child,' said her father, 'in my opinion you ought to use the old one. You had it first. You are used to it and can open your chest with it even in the dark.'

'Then,' said the girl, a delighted expression on her face, 'I must marry this foreign gentleman who so generously and kindly freed me from my spell at very considerable trouble and suffering to himself.'

The poor man she was to have married protested violently, but as soon as the guests heard the story of how the girl's spell had been broken, no one would listen to him. Everyone insisted that she must marry the man who had freed her. They all crowded round the young man, who soon found himself sitting next to the girl who wore his ring, and the very next day they were married. According to the story, they lived for years and years together and had lots of happy children, whom they really rather spoiled, but not enough to stop people liking them.

FIVE

The Magic Mirror

FOR A LONG TIME people had been saying that their
young king ought to marry. He lived in the big palace
surrounded by courtiers and ministers and everyone felt
that he must be lonely and, perhaps, even a little bit
unhappy. Then one day word spread that the king *was*
going to marry.

The news of the great decision was first told to the
court barber, when he was shaving the royal right cheek,
and he, of course, began telling everybody as soon as he
got back to his shop. That night, as they went their
rounds, the night watchmen proclaimed the great news
through the silent streets, causing a great stir in many a
heart, for the king had not yet decided whom he would
marry, but just said that he was actively looking for a
suitable queen and that any girl with the right qualities
would be eligible, whoever she was. Mothers looked at
their daughters, and the daughters looked at themselves
in their mirrors and wondered: 'Could it be me?'

The following morning the court barber's shop was
filled to overflowing. The barber was looking and feeling
very important, for he was the only one who saw the
king every day and he always had the latest news.
People asked him if the king had anyone in mind, whom
he thought would make a suitable queen, and then it

was that the barber dropped the bombshell that set tongues wagging harder than ever.

Looking more knowing than ever, the barber said:

'The king will marry the first girl to pass the test.'

'The test? What test?' everyone wanted to know.

'Not every woman by any means is worthy to marry the king,' said the barber rather pompously. 'So there is to be a test. Everyone who wishes to be considered must first look into my mirror.'

'Why your mirror?'

'You forget that I am under royal licence. I am the court barber, the only man in the kingdom permitted to rub the royal countenance. Besides, my mirror is a magic one and, when a person looks into it, if he or she has done anything wrong or has any blemishes on her character, they will appear as spots on the face. So that whoever thinks herself worthy to marry the king must look into my mirror and let me see what it has to tell.'

Of course, everyone laughed and said what nonsense this was, yet days passed and still no one had come to the barber's shop to look at themselves in the magic mirror. This was all the more surprising as the king was young and good-looking and his subjects loved him, because he was just and kind.

Every morning, when the barber went to the palace to shave the king, the king would ask him if there had been any applicants yet, and the barber would shake his head, and then the king would wonder if he was ever going to find a wife. Why, he asked the barber, had all the previous kings who had lived in that palace enjoyed the company of a wife. How had they found queens so easily?

'Sire,' replied the barber. 'In the old days there was no magic mirror, because one was scarcely required.

People only studied the arts then, but now science has been added to their studies.'

'You mean, then,' said the king, 'that the increase in knowledge has done no good?'

'More than that,' said the barber. 'I mean that people are worse than they used to be.'

'Surely to know is to be wise?' said the king. 'Not always, Sire,' the barber answered. 'The majority of men and women today know both too much and too little, and what people think is wisdom is merely cunning. There is as great a distance between wisdom and cunning, as between heaven and earth.'

'Barber,' said the king, 'you are to find me a wife who shall be as bright as day, as pure as dew and as good as gold. One who shall not be afraid to look into your magic mirror!'

'Sire,' said the barber, 'the only magic about my mirror is what the bad consciences of the women of this city conjure up. I am sure that most simple girls of the countryside would be quite willing to look into my mirror. But could a king marry a humble country girl?'

'A woman who will look into your magic mirror is a pearl without price,' said the king. 'And kings have married humble girls before now – lots of times. I shall do the same. Go and find me a girl who is as I said and I will marry her, even if she is a humble shepherdess. And until you get back I shall not shave, but let my beard grow.'

When he had finished shaving the king, the barber went back home, shut his shop without giving any explanation to his mystified clients, then mounted his horse and rode away.

At every village to which he came the barber went to the old women, those whose daughters had all long since

'Barber, you are to find me a wife.'

married, and asked them which of the village girls was really good and kind and had a sweet disposition; and if some said this one and others said no, not her, but that one, then he knew he must look elsewhere and mounted his horse and rode on.

On the third day, the weary barber came to a village high up in the mountains, and there the women were all agreed that a certain Maria was good and sweet and kind, and the barber knew then he need look no farther.

Maria was a shepherdess and at that time far up the mountainside with her sheep. The barber stabled his horse and set off up the mountain path. Soon he emerged from the belt of trees and, panting and puffing because he was not used to walking far, continued across the close-cropped turf. The path had come to an end, but ahead of him he could see a huddle of rocks round which were some sheep, looking like small white specks because of the distance. Up and up the poor barber toiled. High above his head a lark was singing and higher still a hawk, or perhaps an eagle, was quartering the sky. Some small animal scurried off through a clump of thistles with a sudden noise that made the barber's heart leap into his mouth. He could hear the trickle of water near by. By the time he reached the rocks the poor barber was very glad to sit down. When he had rested he got up; walking on, he found that the rocks formed a rough circle that enclosed a big patch of smooth turf about which sheep were grazing, and there, sitting at the foot of a big boulder was the shepherdess.

She was dressed in simple clothes that were patched and mended, but clean and neat. Her hair was plaited into pigtails that reached to her waist and the eyes she turned on the barber were clear and unafraid. Looking at her the barber decided that seldom had he seen such a pretty girl, and, with a chuckle, he thought how jealous the ladies at court would be when she appeared dressed like them.

Now the barber had been in such a hurry to get to the shepherdess that he had forgotten all about eating, and he realized that he was both very hungry and thirsty, so he asked the shepherdess if she had anything he could eat and she gave him some of her bread and cheese, which was all she had, and he drank from a spring that welled up from the foot of a nearby rock. As he ate, the barber told the shepherdess why he was there. At first she thought he was joking, then she grew serious and wondered. She was not afraid of the mirror, she told him, but how could a simple, humble girl like her marry a king and make him happy? That was what frightened her. Eventually, however, the barber persuaded her to come to the palace and meet the king, so when evening fell they drove the sheep down to the village together and the next morning the girl got up behind the barber on his horse and they rode off down the wide road to the broad highway in the valley and so to the capital, where the news of their approach had preceded them.

The streets were filled with curious, inquisitive people, as they rode to the palace. There the old housekeeper, who looked after the king's servants and saw that the palace was kept clean and dusted, took charge of the girl and led her to her own rooms.

An hour or so later, when the barber was just finishing the account of his search, the door of the room opened and in stepped a girl whom the barber had the greatest difficulty in recognizing as his shepherdess. Her pigtails had been brushed out and her hair put up and fastened with a wonderful jewelled comb. Her dress was simple, but of the richest velvet and bound with a girdle of braided gold. The barber had never seen anyone so lovely, nor, indeed, had the king. He received the girl most kindly and the more he looked at her and the more he talked with her the more he liked her, and in the end he asked her if she would be his wife and his country's queen – provided she first looked into the mirror, about the magic properties of which the barber had already told her.

'Sire,' said the girl. 'We are all sinners in the sight of God, we are told, but I am just a poor shepherdess and have always lived surrounded by my sheep. I know what it is to be loved, because when they sense danger, the sheep come to me for protection. I have no jewels. Wild flowers have been my only ornament and, as often as not, the sky has been my roof and God my friend. So I am certainly not afraid of what I shall see in the magic mirror; and if you wish me to be your queen I shall do my best to be a good one and a better wife.'

Then the king ordered the doors to the great hall to be opened and, taking the shepherdess by her rough little hand, he led her through the groups of courtiers and fine ladies to where the barber had already put up an easel, on which the magic mirror now stood. The great ladies stared and some whispered spitefully, 'How plain she is,' which was far from being the truth. The girl blushed, as anyone would, but she held her head high, and when she looked in the mirror the face that looked back at her was lovely and unblemished.

Then the king announced that the shepherdess was to be his queen and ordered preparations for the wedding to be hastened forward.

After the wedding, when girls came to the barber's shop to ask if they might be allowed to look into the mirror, he would say that it was magic no longer, and people began to wonder if it had ever been so.

SIX

Mirabella

THE TREES WERE PINES, old and lovely, and the ground was a soft mixture of pine needles and sand and felt cool to the feet of the young girl who walked there. Through a gap in the trees she could see a stretch of shore and beyond it the sea, sparkling in the bright sunshine. The girl, Mirabella, would have liked to have gone down to the shore and watched the waves and played among the pools and rocks, but she remembered that her father had once told her that it was dangerous for little girls to go on to the beach alone. And she remembered, too, that her father was dead and, also, that she was hungry.

Mirabella's father had been king of the Silver Isles, a good man whom all his subjects loved. Mirabella was his only child, but he had died and her mother had married again. Now she had a little boy, Gliglu, and in order that he might inherit the kingdom, she had ordered one of her servants to take Mirabella deep into the forest and leave her there, hoping that the wolves would find her and eat her. But when Mirabella was born, her aunt, who was a fairy, had placed round her neck a fairy chain on which was a silver bell, and though Mirabella's mother had often tried to get it off, she had never been able to do so. Somehow the chain would not slip over her head, no scissors could cut it, nor could her mother or any of the servants break it with the strength of their hands; as a result Mirabella still had her silver bell which tinkled gaily wherever she went.

That evening, as Mirabella walked along feeling hungrier and sadder than ever, she happened to stumble and her bell tinkled more loudly than usual, so that a wolf heard it on its way through the forest and came running. When Mirabella saw the wolf, she was very frightened, because she had heard such horrid tales about wolves, but this wolf just said:

> 'Silver bell, silver bell, I am here.
> Tell me what you wish and I shall do it,
> Never fear.'

At first, Mirabella could not believe her ears, but when the wolf repeated his offer of help, she decided that he looked rather kind and said:

'Dear Mr. Wolf, if you could go and fetch my mother, I should be most grateful.'

Mirabella, of course, did not know that it was on her mother's orders she had been taken into the forest and left. The wolf turned and ran off without saying another word, but Mirabella knew that he was going to do as she asked and she began jumping about for joy, making the bell tinkle more loudly than ever. A fox heard the silvery sound and came lolloping up; then it sat back on its haunches and said:

> 'Silver bell, silver bell, I am here.
> Tell me what you wish and I shall do it,
> Never fear.'

Mirabella clapped her hands in delight and said:

'Oh, kind Mr. Fox, I am *so* hungry. Do you think you could get me something to eat?'

Away went the fox, but in a few minutes he was back again carrying a basket inside which Mirabella found a roast chicken and a loaf of bread, a plate and knife and fork, all wrapped up in a clean white napkin. She was delighted with her friend the fox and patted his head and stroked his back, making him wag his thick brush. Then she spread the napkin and began to eat. When she had finished her meal, which she enjoyed very much, the fox picked up the basket and ran off.

Only now, however, did Mirabella realize that she had been thirsty as well as hungry. Having been so successful with her bell, she decided to try it again. No sooner had its silvery tinkle rung out than she heard the tinkling of another bell in the distance, coming nearer and nearer. Standing on tiptoe to crane over some bushes, she saw a stream of water flowing towards her, and sailing on it a small canoe. When it came near, she saw that the canoe had a silver bell like hers fixed to its bows. The canoe stopped beside her, and looking in she saw a silver mug. The canoe was singing a little song:

'Silver bell, silver bell, here I be.
When your mother comes, step in me.'

Mirabella was very puzzled. She still thought that her mother loved her and could not understand why she should get into the canoe when her mother came. But she was too thirsty to worry, and taking the mug she stooped down, filled it with water and drank.

All at once she heard screams in the distance, the screams of a woman who was both frightened and angry.

Nearer and nearer the sounds came, growing louder and louder as they did so, till Mirabella could distinctly hear: 'Help! Help! Let me down, you brute.' Then she saw the wolf come trotting into the clearing and on its back her mother. Every time her mother tried to jump down, the wolf turned its head and bared its teeth, so she stayed where she was. The wolf came running up to Mirabella and deposited her mother at her feet.

Mirabella's mother jumped up and began calling her daughter names and scolding her for having sent the wolf for her. She said that as soon as she got back to her palace she was going to make a law that all wolves were to be killed and that, if Mirabella ever dared show her nose anywhere near the palace again, she would have her put to death too. Poor Mirabella was horrified to discover that her mother did not love her, and perhaps never had, and there was such a wicked look in the queen's eyes that Mirabella stepped into the canoe. 'Where to?' asked the canoe. 'Take me to where my father is,' said Mirabella. At once the canoe began to move, gliding forward so smoothly and steadily that Mirabella was able to stand up and call good-bye to the fox and the wolf. She was just about to call to her mother too, when she saw the queen turn into a tree.

Soon the canoe had reached the coast and sailed on out across the sea. On and on it sailed for four whole days, and then at last land came in sight and Mirabella saw that they were approaching a beautiful island, on which were lots of the kind of palm-tree known as sacred palms. The grass was greener than any grass she could remember, and the sun seemed brighter, though warm rather than hot. As the canoe touched the sand on the shore she saw her father and, stepping out, they fell into each other's arms.

They walked up from the shore together, arm-in-arm. Mirabella thought how lovely it was to be loved and know she was loved. The fronds of the palms waved greetings, humming-birds flitted to and fro: everything seemed to be welcoming her. Her father looked younger and more handsome than she remembered. And so they walked on till they came to a lovely house, not big enough to be called a palace, but a place of light and many windows, set in a wonderful garden in which were beds ablaze with the loveliest and strangest flowers, and there Mirabella lived with her father most happily.

One day, when Mirabella was walking along the shore of this enchanted island, she heard the familiar ringing of a silver bell and, looking out to sea, saw a canoe approaching in which sat her friend the wolf. Gently the canoe ran up on to the wet sand and, jumping out, the wolf told her that her aunt, the fairy, had sent him to fetch her. The prince of the neighbouring country, with whom she had often played when they were both children, wanted her to marry him and help him rule his country wisely and well. Mirabella remembered the prince, of whom she had been very fond, and readily agreed to go back to the world of ordinary mortals. So, having said good-bye to her father and her friends and companions, she went back to the shore and got into the canoe beside the wolf.

As they sailed along across the sparkling sea, the wolf told her what a commotion there had been in the Silver Isles when her mother the queen, who had been turned into a tree, had not come back. Search parties had been sent out, and when she could not be found people had said that the wolves must have eaten her, as the queen had hoped they would eat Mirabella, and the men had all taken their guns and bows and arrows and gone off into the forest intending to kill all the wolves or else drive them out of the country. But then they had come to the place where the oak tree stood, into which the queen had been turned, and someone had seen the queen's golden bracelet round one of the branches. Try as they would, they had been unable to get the bracelet off, so they had fetched a saw and sawn through the branch. As it fell, they had heard a loud shriek, like a cry of pain, and the tree had collapsed and fallen to the ground. Then they knew what had happened and realized that the queen must have been a wicked woman, so they had called off the wolf-hunt and the men had all gone back to their homes to get on with their work. And they had made Gliglu king and, although he was still just a youth, he was being a good king because he took the advice of his aunt, the fairy.

When they reached the mainland there was Gliglu waiting for her with two lovely horses, one with a side-saddle which Mirabella mounted, and together they rode to the palace of the Silver Isles, the wolf trotting along beside them.

There was a great banquet to celebrate Mirabella's return. She sat between her brother and the prince who wanted to marry her, while underneath the table, with its head in her lap, sat the wolf. If ever she felt afraid or doubtful about the future, she had only to look into the wolf's kind brown eyes to be reassured. She fed him scraps and once he smacked his lips so loudly that the prince heard and, looking down, saw the wolf. Then Mirabella had to tell all about the wolf and she asked if the wolf might come and live with them, to which the prince at once agreed. But the wolf said that he thought he would rather stay in the forest, where his real home was; but that if Mirabella should ever need help, she had only to tinkle her silver bell and he would hear it and come to her aid as fast as four enchanted paws could take him, which was very fast indeed.

SEVEN

The Fig Bough

ONCE LONG AGO, when much of the lands of Lusitania was occupied by the Moors, the Emir who lived and ruled in Cordova was Abd-el-Rhaman, a man who did many cruel and stupid things. One of the worst of them was the annual tribute exacted from the peoples of Lusitania. It was not a tribute of money or wine or even of grain, but of human beings. Every year, the captain of the Emir's guard would go to a certain place among the mountains at which roads from the east, the west, the north and the south converged, and there on the day appointed he would collect the tribute, which consisted of one hundred girls, fifty of them of noble birth, fifty of humble origin, but all chosen for their beauty. The only other requirement was that they must be Christians.

It was a wild place, surrounded by rugged crags. The ground was covered with stones and boulders, and so little grew there that no one used the land even for grazing, and there was no house there nor any sign of life, except the eagles that occasionally circled overhead or the tail of some small animal that you might see scurrying off, startled by the unwonted sound of horses' hooves. To this savage place the unfortunate girls chosen for the annual tribute were ordered to come alone on the day appointed, and so greatly did people fear the

Emir and his Moors that the fathers and brothers who escorted the poor girls to the assembly-point used to rein in their horses and take their last farewells of their charges a good distance before they got to the place, leaving the unfortunate girls to travel the last mile or so alone.

It was a June morning many years ago, so many that no one now remembers exactly the year in which this story opens; and though the sun was shining there was grief and sorrow in the house of a certain Dom Ramiro, who owned much of the smiling valley in which his lovely home lay, surrounded by orchards and green meadows. And they had real cause for sorrow, for Dom Ramiro's only daughter had been chosen as one of the fifty noble girls who were to be sent to the land of the Moors as part of the country's annual tribute. For years now Dom Ramiro had feared just this. For him the swift arrival of spring had not been a time for rejoicing, but the herald of weeks of anxiety and sleepless nights, till those responsible had drawn up the list of the year's victims and he could breathe again, because the name of Mecia, his only daughter, was not on it. But now the blow had fallen. At first, Dom Ramiro had been like one stunned, then in a burst of fury he had sworn that he would not let it happen, that he would fight and stop them taking his daughter. But whom would he fight? The other fathers whose daughters had not yet been chosen and who would insist that his must go? The Emir's men? How could he hope to accomplish anything, his daughter asked, and finally calmed him down and persuaded him to resign himself, as she had already resigned herself, and hope for a miracle – which indeed was the only thing that could save her.

And so, when the time came, Dom Ramiro mounted

D

his horse and rode with his daughter up the road towards the country of the Moors and then in among the lowering mountains themselves. Here and there they could see others all making in the same direction, in smaller or larger groups, the girls all sad, their faces stained with tears, the men grim-faced and angry, knuckles white in the hand that clenched the hilts of their swords. And so they had come to the great boulder round which the road divided to become one again on the other side, and there they had said good-bye, scarcely daring to look each other in the face, and Mecia had dismounted and handed her father her horse's reins, turned and walked on deeper into the mountains to where, less than a mile away, the Emir's men would be waiting.

The sun shone down out of a blue sky, but there was no sunshine in the heart of Mecia, for all her loveliness, as she walked on, eyes on the ground so that none should see the tears that formed on the long lashes and so fell to the stony ground. But there was no one else in the immediate vicinity and Mecia was grateful that she could be alone, till she could fight down the lump in her throat that was threatening to choke her. Then, all at once she thought she could hear someone singing. That anyone could sing so gay and carefree a song in such a place seemed so incongruous that she dismissed the idea as ridiculous. But, yes! There it was again, now quite distinct. The next moment, round a bluff came a horse and rider. The rider who was young and unhelmeted was singing, but stopped abruptly when he caught sight of the girl. His eyes never left her as he approached; then he reined his horse in and asked:

'Who are you and why are you here among the mountains alone? And, above all, why do you look so sad, when the sun is shining and summer is here?'

'Tell me first who you are, and why you are in this dangerous place?' said Mecia.

'Dangerous,' the man said in a surprised voice. 'Why dangerous? There is no danger here!'

'Don't you know?' Mecia asked. 'Look at those other groups, at the girls all heading in the one direction. Don't you know?'

But the young man had no idea what it was all about, and when Mecia told him he was appalled and his face set in grim angry determination.

'You must go no farther,' he said. 'And tell the other girls to do the same. You must all wait here.'

'And what do you think you are going to be able to do?' Mecia asked.

'I shall tell the Emir's men that you are not coming. That they are to have no tribute this year.'

'But they'll kill you. There will be thirty of them and you are alone. You would just be throwing your life away.'

'Life would be no good to me if I were to live it with this picture before my eyes,' he waved his hand to include the girl before him and all the others they could see, 'and the knowledge that I had not tried to help. I would rather die than live like that.'

And, saying that, the young man took his helmet from the pommel of his saddle and placed it on his head. Then he loosened his sword in its scabbard and wheeling his horse round, galloped off up the road towards the waiting Moors.

The captain of the Moors looked up as he heard the clatter of horseshoes on the stony ground and a look of astonishment and anger came over his face as he saw a horseman, whose armour and accoutrements proclaimed him a Christian, galloping into the open space. His face

. . . towards the waiting Moors.

darkened still further when the rider reined in his horse abruptly, and standing in his stirrups called out in a voice that rang and echoed in that confined space:

'Hallo, you Moors! I am here to tell you that I have ordered the girls to go back to their homes. The Emir shall have no human tribute this year.'

'And who are you, who dares to defy the Emir?' asked the Moorish captain, a cruel sardonic smile on his face.

'I am Goesto Ansures and I will not permit this evil thing.'

'Permit,' laughed the Moorish Captain. 'I, sir, shall permit you to die – now.' And at a sign from their captain, two of the thirty Moors waiting by a tall fig-tree spurred their horses towards the young knight. But Ansures was not content to await their attack. He too urged his horse forward, and as his spurs touched its flanks the fiery stallion took a great leap, nostrils flaring. The three met in the confined space between two great boulders, which hampered the two Moors but favoured the knight. Nor did Ansures fight alone. His horse fought with him. Rearing up, its iron-shod hooves flailing, it crushed the skull of one of the Moors, while its rider's sword bit deep into the body of the other. Then Ansures called out in a fierce voice: 'Come and fight, you Moors. Come and taste my Christian steel!'

Never had those mountains looked down upon such a combat as that which then ensued. Furious at the death of their comrades, a dozen Moors spurred to get at the Christian knight who dared defy the Emir, but their very numbers only helped their adversary, for the Moors' horses jostled each other, and the crush made it difficult for them to swing their scimitars, which could only slash and cut, not thrust. Rearing and plunging, the knight's stallion accounted for almost as many of the Moors as did its rider's sword, which rose and fell, stabbed and thrust, while horses screamed and men groaned and cried aloud. Soon the watching Moors could see that the Christian knight had triumphed yet again, for now only one Moor out of the twelve was left and he hard pressed, so others spurred to his assistance, and again the fight became fast and furious, but none could penetrate that iron wall of flailing hooves and swirling sword that confronted the angry Moors. Soon there was a veritable rampart of bodies and behind this the young knight fought till he thought his sword would drop from his aching hand, but all at once there were no more blows to parry, no foe to fight, and looking through the swirling dust he saw that only one Moor was left, the captain, astride his horse by the fig-tree.

Putting his spurs to his horse, the young knight leaped the rampart of the dead in front of him and galloped towards the Moor, who drew his scimitar and awaited the onslaught. As the two men closed there was a resounding clash and the young knight's sword caught on the Moor's scimitar, broke off at the hilt and the blade went flying through the air.

'Surrender, Infidel,' called the Moor exultantly.

'Never,' replied the young knight. 'I don't need a sword to kill a Moor,' saying which he seized hold of a bough of the fig-tree and wrenched it off. Then, using the bough as a club, with one great blow he knocked the Moor's scimitar from his hand and with a second sent his adversary tumbling out of the saddle on to the ground, from which the trampling hooves of the stallion made sure that he would never again rise. Slowly the young knight turned and rode back the way he had come.

Beside a ring of stones he found the group of girls. Faces pale, their eyes looked up at him in mute inquiry, noting the bough that he still grasped, the blood on his armour and his horse.

'You are free,' the young knight told them. 'The Emir in Cordova shall have no tribute this year. You are free and can go home; all, that is, except one,' and he pointed to Mecia.

Then riding up to Mecia he dismounted stiffly and, standing before her, so that he could gaze deep into her eyes and heart, he said:

'You are not free, because I want you for my wife. Nor am I free, because you hold my heart.'

And Mecia looked up at him and said:

'This time I shall be a very willing captive – and need no rescuer.'

So, together, they set off back to the house among the orchards that was Mecia's home, where a man's face brightened in uncomprehending joy when he saw them. And never has a horse been groomed and bedded down with greater loving care than was Goesto Ansures's stallion that night. Never has a horse been given sweeter hay or nicer oats than the great stallion had, when Dom Ramiro fed and watered it himself, insisting that no groom or stable lad should entertain his daughter's other rescuer.

A few days later, the great stallion set out on another journey, taking Goesto Ansures and his young wife, Mecia, to their new home.

EIGHT

The Princess and the Pigeons

MUCH OF THE Atlantic coast of Lusitania is rocky and rather desolate, and the people who live along it are poor, hard though they may work. Once there was a young fisherman called Pedro who lived in one of the hamlets on a dangerous stretch of this coast. He was good-looking and kind, and lived with his widowed mother. Sometimes he would dream of making such a catch that he could buy his mother all the things that life had denied her, and perhaps even have something over for himself. But in his heart of hearts he never imagined that he would ever really be rich. One morning Pedro left home early, intending to visit some rock-pools he knew, that formed when the tide was at its lowest. The sun was shining, making the wet sand sparkle; everywhere there was the freshness of early morning. The crying of birds hung over the cliffs and the wide stretch of beach was littered with rocks studded with limpets and sea-anemones that glowed and sparkled like precious stones. Pedro set off along the beach heading for the first of his pools, but as he drew near he saw that someone had got up even earlier than he, for there, seated by the pool, feet trailing in the water, was a girl. She was magnificently dressed, and her hand held a jewelled comb with which she was combing her long jet-black hair. Pedro's first thought was that she must be a mermaid, so he hid behind a rock because he was afraid that if she saw him, she might cast a spell on him. So there he crouched, close enough to see all she did and hear the song she was singing. What he heard made his jaw drop in astonishment and his eyes grow wide, for it told him that the girl he was watching was the daughter of the King of Aragon, who had ordered her execution because she had refused to marry an evil knight. She had been taken to this lonely part of the coast, but there her executioners had not had the heart to kill one who was so young and pretty, so they had left her there to fend for herself and returned to tell the king that they had accomplished their mission. The song also told of messengers who brought the girl food, but Pedro could see no sign of them, nor of food either.

Pedro did not know what to do. Common sense told him that if he helped someone a king wished to see dead, he would risk the king sending people to kill him too; on the other hand he could not leave the girl in such a desperate plight. As he crouched behind his rock, trying to pluck up courage to go and speak to the girl, he heard a whirr of wings above his head, and looking up saw two pure white pigeons holding between them in their beaks a thin golden rod on which was hung a small basket. Lower and lower the pigeons flew and finally alighted beside the girl, who spoke to them cooingly and stroked their lovely feathers with the tips of her fingers. Then she emptied the basket which contained things to eat and Pedro could tell that she must have been hungry, because she gobbled it all up in no time. Then the girl licked her fingers, as even princesses do when they are not being watched, and began to sing again. Pedro listened and had just heard her say that she wished she could be a bird, when to his utter amazement, he saw the girl turn into a white bird, just like a swan except that on its head was a small golden crown. Then she spread her wings and flew off, attended by the two pigeons. Pedro gazed after the swan as it rose higher and higher, before turning and heading out to sea.

Pedro stood up, not knowing what to make of it all; then he happened to glance out to sea where, quite close in, though he had not seen her before, was a great ship. Her deck was so bright and polished it looked as if it was made of gold, and the planks in her sides were made of ivory fastened with golden nails. The ropes of the rigging were made of silver thread, the sails of silk and the mast and yards of the finest sandal-wood. Above this ship, the three birds were circling, then down they flew and alighted. As their feet touched the deck they vanished and, instead, Pedro saw the princess seated on a great throne-like chair beneath a magnificent awning, and at her feet two maidens squatted on velvet cushions.

This was too much for poor Pedro. He panicked and, setting off at a run, headed inland, away from the sea where such frightening things were happening. It was not long before the ship was out of sight, but in his ear a voice kept repeating: 'Don't run away. A king doesn't run away.' But Pedro paid no attention and just ran on and on, till, in the depths of the forest he simply had to stop and fling himself down, gasping for breath. As he lay there, he heard someone say, quite distinctly: 'Pedro you are going to be the king, but don't tell anyone.' This extraordinary remark made Pedro sit up, and then he noticed that he was no longer wearing his old fisher-man's clothes, but a magnificent coat trimmed with gold lace, and elegant breeches. Seeing that, Pedro realized that magic was being worked on him. The princess, he told himself, must have been a mermaid after all and had seen him and put a spell on him. But he wondered, as he fingered his splendid clothes, whether they were real or if he was just seeing things. Altogether the situation was too much for young Pedro and, getting to his feet, he did as you or I would have done – he hurried home.

But when he reached his little fishing village, nobody seemed to know him. Those of his friends he saw in the street just bowed and showed him such deference that he felt sure they were trying to make a fool of him. At last he got home and ran inside. His mother was frying some fish, and when she saw a grand gentleman standing in her kitchen she took the pan off the fire, curtsied and said: 'Sir, this is too humble a house to give you accom-modation or refreshment. Let me take you to the priest nearby.' Pedro tried to protest and explain who he was, but as he opened his mouth his tongue lolled out and, instead of speaking, all he could do was to make gurgling noises, while he gesticulated wildly. His poor mother thought her fine visitor must be mad and hustled him out of her house.

Outside, quite a crowd had collected to see the noble stranger. Among the crowd was the priest. When they saw Pedro gesticulating and making his weird noises, they decided he must be mad and perhaps dangerous, so they all took to their heels and ran. Realizing that the spell was preventing him making himself known, Pedro turned sadly away and set off down the road for the next town.

Before long Pedro noticed a big gate made of gold, and beyond it a beautiful garden where an old gardener was at work. Something prompted him to stop and, opening his mouth, he heard himself say: 'Open the gate, gardener, I have come to speak to my love.' The gardener looked up and said: 'Come in, sir, you are Don Pedro, as I can see.'

'What high balconies,' Pedro exclaimed looking up at the palace wall. 'They must be a hundred feet up. Tell me, does the princess ever come out on them?'

'She comes every evening to feel the cool breeze,' the gardener said, 'and she comes alone.'

'I will stay and help you water the flowers,' Pedro said, 'and if she asks you who I am, say that I am your son come back from abroad.'

And sure enough that evening, at her usual time, the princess appeared on her favourite balcony and seeing Pedro, who was busy watering the flowers, she beckoned to him and said, 'Come a little closer. I wish to speak with you.'

'Is it true that you wish to speak with me?' Pedro asked.

'No mirror ever reflected the truth more correctly than those words, my desire,' the princess answered.

'Here I am, then,' said Pedro going closer, 'command me as you would your slave, but please give me some water, for I am thirsty.'

The princess poured some water into a silver cup and handed it to Pedro, who said:

'In this bright mirror of pure water, which reflects your form, I quench my heart's great thirst.'

'Do you see that building at the end of the garden?' asked the princess. 'That is where you will stay

'Come in, Sir, you are Don Pedro.'

tonight; but if you ever tell anyone what you see there, you will cause me great trouble and put yourself in danger.'

Pedro promised to keep all that he saw a secret, and saying good night to the princess, he hurried off to the building to which she had pointed. Inside he found a long marble passage down which he walked. It was lined with marble pillars, behind which he occasionally thought he caught a glimpse of a pretty girl hurrying past. As he drew near a richly carved fountain he saw a girl talking to a Moor in impassioned tones, but a moment later he discovered that they were both statues. On he walked, the passage becoming more and more magnificent, and at last he reached the end, where there was a door. Opening this he found himself standing on a marble quay against which waves were lapping. Looking out to sea, he saw the beautiful ivory and gold ship to which the enchanted birds had flown that morning, approaching at speed. She sailed right in, and as she came alongside the quay a sailor jumped ashore and made her fast with a golden hawser. Then, turning to Pedro, the sailor said:

'I am glad you have not kept us waiting. Our royal mistress is anxious to consult you, as one of her pigeons has broken its right wing and if you cannot cure it the princess will starve to death.'

Pedro at once stepped on board. The sailor cast off, and the ship put out to sea again. Before long they were approaching the part of the coast where Pedro lived and which he knew so well. And there, sitting on the sand, was the princess, nursing one of her white pigeons. As he stepped ashore, the princess looked up and said: 'Don Pedro, a stranger dared to enter my royal father's garden and in helping water the flowers trod on the wing of my favourite pigeon and broke it.'

'Princess,' Pedro said, 'the intruder was probably looking for you and had no idea he had hurt your bird.'

'That's beside the point,' the princess said. 'My pigeon is wounded and you must cure her. Cut out my heart and steep the bird in my warm blood. When I am dead, throw my body into the sea.'

'But I can't do that!' Pedro exclaimed aghast. 'I would rather die myself than hurt you!'

'But if you really cared for me, you would do as I asked,' said the princess.

'Princess, I cannot and will not kill you; but I will do anything else you tell me,' said Pedro.

'All right then; if you won't kill me, take the pigeon back with you – you see, I know it was you who was in my father's garden – and tomorrow evening, when you see the princess whom you saw today, you must kill her and let her blood fall on the pigeon.'

What was Pedro to do? Having promised the princess that he would do anything she told him except kill her, he could not now go back on his word, but he certainly had no wish to kill anyone. He was in great trouble and felt very down-hearted. Then, taking the pigeon very gently from the princess, he went back on board the ship, which set sail at once. Pedro was feeling so depressed; he just sood staring at the deck, glum and miserable, and, before he knew what was happening the ship had arrived back at the marble quay.

Pedro landed and made his way back down the long corridor with its pillars to the garden, where he found the old gardener again watering the flowers.

'Will the princess come this evening?' Pedro asked, hoping that the answer would be no.

'The Princess loves the sea breeze and she will come out tonight, for her noble lover will be waiting for her.'

'Who is the princess's lover?' Pedro asked.

'If you will help me water the flowers, I'll tell you,' the old man said.

Pedro was quite glad to help, so putting the pigeon down in a safe place, where he was sure it could come to no harm, he began helping to water the flowers. When they had been working away for a few minutes in silence, the old gardener suddenly spoke:

'Once there were seven pigeons who said: "Seven pigeons are we and we might all be mated with seven other pigeons, but as it is, we have to remain just seven pigeons." '

'Perhaps,' Pedro put in, 'but I want to know who the princess's lover is.'

The gardener paid no attention to this interruption, except that he started all over again:

'Once there were seven pigeons who said . . .'

'Be quiet!' Pedro shouted. 'I don't want to hear that nonsense. I want to know who the princess's noble lover is. Tell me, or it will be the worse for you.'

'Sir,' said the gardener, looking up with a very serious expression on his face, 'once there were seven pigeons . . .'

'Oh, shut up and get on with your watering,' Pedro said in disgust.

'And yet there were seven pigeons once,' the old man said, 'but now the last of them is gone, because the noble lover has been false to his trust,' and he looked very cunningly at Pedro.

Pedro turned and looked at the place where he had put the pigeon. It had gone! He felt furiously angry and turned, and raised his hand as though to hit the gardener, but to his astonishment the gardener had disappeared too.

Poor Pedro felt desperately unhappy, for he could not do what he had promised and now he would probably never see the princess again. Then the world went black and Pedro fell to the ground in a faint.

As he came to, he heard a mocking voice saying, 'Once there were seven pigeons . . .' but it was not the voice of the old gardener. Starting up, Pedro saw standing beside him the princess who had given him the cup of water.

'Why do you tease me?' he said. 'I don't want to hear about those beastly pigeons.'

'Don Pedro,' said the princess. 'I must tell you that the old gardener is a magician who has possessed himself of my last means of regaining my liberty, so that I am in his power. Isn't it true that you came here intending to kill me?'

'I was under a vow to do so,' Pedro replied, 'but I cannot do that, though I would rather slay you than do you a more grievous injury.'

'Go back then to the unhappy lady you left on the seashore and tell her that you have broken your promise,' said the princess.

'How sorry I am that I was ever destined to be king,' Pedro exclaimed. 'I was much happier when I was just a poor fisherman.'

'Why Pedro, there is a full moon tonight and at midnight the wicked magician's power will be at its weakest, so perhaps you will be able to save me. That is, if you have the courage to meet him in the gardens at midnight.'

E

'I'm prepared for anything,' Pedro answered, 'and I'm not afraid of that old man.'

'Well then,' said the princess, 'when the magician sees you again, he will start telling you about the seven pigeons. You must listen and, when he has finished, you must tell him that once there were seven wives who had only one husband and that they are waiting outside to see him. He will get very angry at that; but, if you are not afraid, you may be able to free me.'

Pedro promised that he would do as she said and the princess left him and went back into the palace with the high balconies.

Night fell and the fireflies glowed brighter and brighter as the darkness increased. At just about midnight the magician appeared, watering the flowers. Noticing Pedro, he came up to him and at once began:

'Once there were seven pigeons . . .'

Pedro listened till he had finished and then said:

'Quite so, but once upon a time there were seven wives who had only one husband and they are waiting outside to see him.'

At this, the magician fell into a fury. He dropped his watering-can and waved his fists about, shouting and stamping his feet, but Pedro just repeated what he had said, then the magician seemed to collapse.

'I am defeated,' he sighed. 'But if you can induce the spirits of my seven wives to go back to their graves, I will give you what you want, which, I know, is the princess.'

'Give me the princess first,' Pedro said, 'then I will try to free you of your wives.'

'Take her then,' said the magician, 'here she is and don't forget about my wives.'

At that moment the princess came out of the palace

and Pedro hurried towards her, and as he did so, he saw that she and the princess on the shore were the same. Together they walked out of the garden and through the golden gate, back to the world of men, where they were married and crowned king and queen.

NINE

The Princess in the Tower

THIS IS THE STORY of a wicked man, and, what is worse, of one who was a king and should have known better. He was king of a part of Lusitania where distances were great and people happy. This king was a widower and had three daughters. As the years passed and the three made their own friends and needed less of their father's companionship, the king began to feel lonely and felt that he would like another queen to occupy the second throne that always looked so empty standing there beside his in the audience chamber. So, after thinking things over, he went on a visit to a neighbouring kingdom, where a princess lived whom he had met and admired, intending to ask her to marry him. The princess was only too happy to marry the king and become queen of his country, but being over-indulged and thoroughly spoilt she thought only of her own comfort and convenience and, before she said yes, she asked the king what he was going to do with his daughters. She did not want the bother of looking after three teenage girls, let alone the trouble of finding husbands for them and arranging their weddings. Now the king, as we know, was a bad man and, though he had always been nice to his daughters, he had never really loved them, and so he said to the princess:

'If you feel that my daughters will be a hindrance to our happiness, I'll soon dispose of them. I'll send them away to a place where you will never see them or hear about them. They need never worry you.'

Happy with that assurance, the princess agreed to marry the king, who gave her a magnificent engagement ring and then set off back to his own kingdom to make arrangements for the new queen. The first thing he had to do was to get rid of his daughters, and he thought that he had better do this before telling anyone of his decision to marry again.

Now the king's domains included part of the coast where the town of Faro stands, and there was a tall tower from which, in the old days, guards kept watch for pirates from Africa or raiding Norsemen from the lands far to the north. This was called the tower of Montecorvo.

One day, soon after his return, the king sent for his daughters and said to them:

'Get yourselves ready for a little expedition. I am going to take you to the tower of Montecorvo and there I'll show you something you've never seen before in all your lives.'

The girls, eager for any little adventure and quite unsuspecting, because they loved their father and could not even dream that he should ever do them any harm, got themselves ready and off they all went.

It took them the best part of a day to reach the tower and the girls were quite tired when they arrived, so the king took them inside and told them to rest, while he went to a nobleman who lived nearby, who was one of his subjects, to arrange for servants and food to be sent to the tower. It was suggested they should explore the tower afterwards and he would then show them the wonderful thing they had come to see. The three trusting girls agreed, of course, and flung themselves down on couches to rest their weary limbs. Then the king went out and fastened the gate of the tower so securely that his daughters could not possibly get out. Nor was there any other means of escape, for the tower was built rather like a lighthouse and there was no window or other opening in its sheer walls for a height of sixty feet. And so the king rode away.

When their father did not return the girls became worried, and, when they found the gate so securely fastened that they could not open it whatever they did, they were dismayed and really frightened. At first they could not believe that their father had left them there on purpose, but when the next day men came with baskets of food, which they pushed in through a tiny hatch in the postern – far too small for even the slimmest girl to squeeze through – the girls realized that the king must have planned it all, and they were very sad indeed.

Every day the king sent men with food to his daughters, but on his wedding day he forgot to give the usual order and when he and the queen went on their honeymoon he never gave his three daughters another thought. Fortunately there was a well in the little courtyard of the tower, so that the three girls were not tormented with thirst, but they became hungrier and hungrier. Hard as they looked, they could find nothing to eat anywhere in the great tower and soon they were really starving. After some days the oldest sister died, and a day later the second eldest also died, so that only the youngest was left. When she woke up that morning to find that she was the only one still alive, she had just the strength left to climb up to the flat roof of the tower, and, looking over the parapet, she saw a ship sailing past, so close that she could hear the voices of the men on deck and see their faces.

The princess shouted as loudly as she could and waved her scarf to attract their attention. Her voice was so faint, owing to her weakness, that the sailors could not hear her; but someone saw her waving and the princess watched one of the sailors run below, after which an officer, perhaps the captain, came on deck, the ship turned head into the wind, the sails came down with a run and a boat was lowered and rowed to land.

Briefly, shouting from the top of the tower, the princess told them of her predicament. One of the sailors managed to climb up to her, while the others went back to the ship and fetched axes and hammers with which they eventually broke down the great gate that gave access to the tower.

The sailors and their captain were horrified that any-one as young and lovely as the princess should have been treated in such a cruel way. While some of them stayed behind to dig a grave for the two princesses who had died, the others took the youngest princess aboard. With her she had only a small chest into which she had put her sisters' clothes and jewels. The captain received her most kindly, and the ship's cook made her the nicest things he knew how to make, and before long the princess was feeling much better. When you are young, you cannot despair for long and soon the princess was looking forward to the future, though she had no idea what she was going to do.

The ship that had rescued her was sailing on to a

. . . and waved her scarf.

distant land, so it was decided that they would put the princess ashore at the next port they came to along the coast. This happened to be the capital of a neighbouring kingdom. The sailors helped the princess ashore and left her standing there with her chest of clothes. Now, for the first time, the horror of her predicament came over her. Here she was in a strange country with no friends or relations to help. No home to go to and no money. Almost on the point of tears, she stood there wondering what to do, when she saw an old woman coming towards her. The old woman had a kind, crinkley face and nice smiling eyes and the princess felt sure that she would help, so she went up to her and asked the old woman if she knew of anyone who could give her a meal and a bed for the night, adding that she was willing to work for it.

'If it's work you want,' said the old woman, 'come and help me draw water and carry it to the house where I work; they will give you a meal there and in the evening you can come back with me to my little cottage.'

'What house do you work for?' the princess asked.

'Oh, I draw water for the king's palace,' answered the old woman.

Hearing that the princess agreed to help her, but as she could not do such work in her fine clothes, she went to the old woman's cottage where, finding a horse-skin, she made herself a rough garment with it. In this new outfit nobody would have taken her for a princess.

Every day the princess went to the well and helped the old woman draw water and carry the buckets and pitchers to the palace, where people began calling her Horse-skin, because of her clothes.

One day, as she came into the palace yard, walking lightly and gracefully with a pitcher of water balanced on her head, it struck a page, who had often noticed her before and been impressed by her beauty and the elegance of her figure and bearing, that she had not been born to such drudgery and that there must be some mystery about her. Going up to her, the page said most respectfully:

'Do you know that our good king is going to give a ball every night for three nights running, so that he may choose a wife from among the guests? The prettiest girl is to get a prize and to the girl of his choice the king will give a ring. I wish you would go.'

'What business has a poor girl like me at court balls?' the princess said. 'That's all right for grand ladies, but I shall be so tired tonight that I shall only want to go to bed and sleep.'

That is what the princess said, but as soon as she had done her work she went home and, taking off her dress of horse's skin, she washed all over and put on one of the lovely dresses that had belonged to her elder sister. Then she sneaked out and, going to the palace, slipped into the brilliantly lit ballroom without being announced. Soon heads were turning and people whispering as they asked each other who this beautiful girl was. The king was not long in noticing her too, and he came straight up and led her away to dance with him. In fact he made all the other ladies very jealous because he danced with her so often. He paid her the nicest compliments and asked her various things about herself most of which she cleverly avoided answering. Towards morning the princes managed to slip away without being seen, and a few hours later she was back at work dressed in her horse-skin gown again, drawing and carrying water for the palace.

As she went to and fro, she again met the page and he again told her that she ought to go to the ball that night, but the princess just pretended to be annoyed and told him that balls were not for her, and that that evening would find her in the old woman's cottage sleeping the sleep of the just as usual. But that is just what it didn't. As soon as the princess returned home, she slipped out of her rough horse-skin and put on another dress that had been her second sister's and which set off her beauty even better than the other had.

As soon as she entered the ballroom on this second night, several men came hurrying up to claim dances from her, but as they were laughing and chatting, the king thrust his way through and taking the princess by the hand, he led her away to dance with him. This time he danced practically every dance with her. They laughed and joked together and talked about all sorts of things, serious and gay, but the king did not like to ask her outright who she was; so that when she slipped away again without being seen just before the ball ended, he was no wiser than before.

In the morning, the princess was back at her job, and again the page came up to her and said:

'Oh, Horse-skin, do come to the third ball tonight. It's the last one and tonight the king is to give the ring to the girl he thinks prettiest and admires most. I wish you had been there last night, the grand ladies were so jealous because the king would scarcely look at them or talk to them; he had time only for a lovely and myster-ious girl, who had been at the previous ball too, though nobody knows anything about her. People say the king has quite lost his heart to her. I saw her too. She is awfully like you. She has a lovely smile and coral lips and the same lovely eyes as you. I only wish I were a prince and could marry her.'

'Oh, don't talk to me of dancing. I'm too tired to dance. I can only go to bed at night,' said the princess and walked off.

That evening the princess again changed as soon as she got back to the old woman's cottage, but this time she put on her own gown, which suited her best of all. Again she entered the ballroom unannounced and as she threaded her way through the throng of guests, even the most jealous had to admit that she was the loveliest girl there, lovelier than any of the princesses, duchesses or other noble ladies. The king was quite captivated and would dance with no one else. Then, at the time appointed for the great decision, he gave her the ring to show that he had chosen her and wished her to be his wife and queen. He told several of his courtiers to see where she went, if she should try to slip away again, but even so the princess managed to distract their attention and get away back to the old woman's cottage unobserved.

The next morning the king told his courtiers to find out who the girl was to whom he had given his ring, where she lived and all about her; but no one could tell them anything. Nor could she be found. The king ordered the whole of his country to be searched, but it was all in vain. Nobody appeared to have seen the mysterious girl since the night of the third ball, and nobody knew who she was. This made the king so sad and dispirited that he felt quite ill. His physicians gave him medicines and pills, which did him no good at all, and people began to fear that their king was going to die. The king himself did not care if he did die; to him life without the mysterious girl with whom he had fallen in love held nothing at all, and he just lay in bed feeling more and more sad and dejected.

The physicians sent for four nurses to help look after the king, two for the day and two for the night. One day shortly afterwards, Horse-skin met one of the nurses carrying a bowl of broth, and asked her how the king was.

'He is really very ill,' said the nurse, 'because he loves this girl so much that he does not wish to live without her. This soup is for him, but it will do him no good. The only thing that will help him is for the girl to come back. It is very cruel of her to behave like this.'

Horse-skin had really been longing to make herself known to the king, but had not known how to do it. Hearing what the nurse said she became desperate, and taking the king's ring from the secret pocket where she kept it, she dropped it into the bowl of broth while the nurse was looking the other way.

You can imagine how surprised the king was to find his ring at the bottom of the bowl of soup. He asked the nurse how it had got there, but she could offer no explanation and swore that the only person she had met was the poor water-girl, Horse-skin. The king then felt sure that Horse-skin must know the secret so he sent for her and, shortly afterwards, she was ushered into his room.

If the king had not been so preoccupied with his own sorrow he would probably have taken a good look at the girl everyone called Horse-skin and all his questions would have been answered. But as it was, he scarcely glanced at her as he told her to tell him how the ring had got into his bowl of broth. She replied that she had dropped it into the bowl. The king then asked her where she had got it from.

'If your majesty will allow me to retire for a few minutes, I will tell you who gave me the ring, the moment I get back.'

The king agreed to this and Horse-skin hurried away to put on her own proper clothes. The king did not have long to wait. Looking up as his page opened the door, the king saw a girl step into his room. Not a girl, but *his* girl, the mysterious lovely girl to whom he had given his ring at the third ball.

'Does your majesty know me now?' the princess asked.

'Of course, I do. You are the sweet and lovely girl to whom I gave the ring.'

'I am,' said the princess, 'and I am also the one who dropped it into your bowl of broth, your humble servant, Horse-skin.'

The king was thoroughly mystified, yet overjoyed to have found his sweetheart, and he insisted that the princess sit on his bed while she told him the story that explained the mystery. The princess wept a little, as she told him all that had happened to her, because it brought it back so vividly. The king was furious and wanted to declare war on the princess's father and punish him, but the princess persuaded him not to, insisting that she would far rather forget it all and begin life again with the king.

The king refused to let the princess go back to the old woman's cottage, and instead installed her in a suite of beautifully furnished apartments that had once been his mother's, while the preparations for the wedding were hurried on. Everybody was delighted that the king had at last found himself a wife and happiness, both because they were fond of him and also because he could now attend to affairs of state again.

TEN

The Subterranean Passage

ON THE RIVER DOURO there is a town called Freixo. It is ringed by hills that are capped with snow in wintertime, when the winds whistle down the valleys between them, howling and shrieking so horribly that the sound makes people shudder and wonder whether the Enchanted Moor is out on the prowl again. Near the town is an almost perpendicular bluff with a jumble of huge rocks lining the foot of it, a windy place and a noisy one when a storm is raging. It is here that, many years ago, the Enchanted Moor had a palace, smaller than the great palace of the Alhambra at Granada, but just as beautiful and even more famous, because in its stable was lodged the donkey on which the prophet Mohammed was supposed to have ascended to Paradise. Evidently the donkey had not found Paradise to its liking, since it had made its way back and been found grazing near the palace one morning, when the people of Freixo were on their way to the mosque. This palace was called the Alcazar of Al Rachid, the maker of spells.

Far away, on the other side of the forest, was the home of a rich farmer, who had a daughter called Maria. She was as beautiful as she was good, at least her parents thought so, and so did a young man who was in love with her, as she was with him. One day, when

Maria was working in the fields, as she always did even though her father was rich, the great Al Rachid saw her from the fringe of the trees. After that he used to come back again and again to watch her and to think how lovely she was. He would have married her, but he knew that he could not do that, both because she was a Christian and because she was already in love with someone else. Again and again he came back to watch her from the cover of the trees and in the end he decided that he would try to capture her and carry her off by force.

One evening Maria did not return to the farm at the end of the day. Her parents became more and more anxious, as they looked for her everywhere. She could not be found. Nobody had seen her. Then Maria's parents sent messages to all their friends and they organized search parties which combed the country for miles around; but there was not a sign nor a trace of Maria to be seen.

After that they knew. Al Rachid had got her. It was not that anyone had seen Al Rachid that day, but the Moors were able to work magic, everybody knew that, magic so powerful that it could build subterranean passages which either remained open or closed up behind the user, making it impossible to chase and catch him. Maria's parents went straight to the local wise-woman, and she lit a fire of pine needles and after gazing into it intently for a long time, she told them that Maria had indeed been carried off by Al Rachid and also the direction in which the girl and her captor had gone. Again the searchers mounted their horses and galloped off in the direction indicated.

For two days they rode, pressing on as fast as ever they could, but they never caught even a glimpse of

F

Maria or her captor, nor did they see even so much as a hoof-print. Then, all at once, they thought they could hear the sound of galloping hoofs, yet they could not see a horse. The sound seemed to be ahead of them, and then it was right underneath them, and they realized that Al Rachid was using a magic subterranean passage. That being so – as it was – they were helpless. All they could do was follow the sound and hope. This they did and soon came into sight of the Alcazar of Freixo and realized that the subterranean passage would lead right into the palace itself.

Not being Moors, the searchers would have been killed if they had dared to venture inside the town. They now had no hope of being able to rescue poor Maria, and sadly and reluctantly they turned their horses' heads and rode back home. What else could

. . . the great

they do? No infidel was ever allowed into the town of Freixo, let alone through the gates of the palace of the great Al Rachid. The band of searchers was far too small to attempt to take the town by storm, and being Christians they could not have used the subterranean passage, even if they could have found it. The spell on it made that impossible. All this they told to Maria's parents when they returned home.

Maria's father wondered and wondered what on earth they could do, and then one day he had an idea. A baby boy had just been born in the village and he went to his parents and had a talk with them. As a result, the baby's parents agreed they would not have their son baptized at the usual time, but wait until he was grown up. This meant that being unbaptized he would be able to use the subterranean passage and, if

chid saw her.

he were big and strong and brave, perhaps rescue Maria. It also meant that poor Maria would have long years of captivity to endure, but there was nothing else that they could do.

Years passed. When the boy was thirteen, big and strong and almost like a man, they told him why he had not been baptized and what they hoped he would be able to do. He was a stout-hearted boy and one who was never averse to anything dangerous. The rich farmer had seen to it that he had had lessons in arms and knew how to use a sword. He readily agreed to try and rescue Maria from the clutches of the Moor. Maria's father gave him his best sword and stoutest shield, and off he went. First he went to the cottage of the wise-woman, who was to help him find the subterranean passage, and together they walked off into the forest. After an hour or so they came to an aged, gnarled oak and there the wise-woman stopped. First she called out in a loud voice: 'Here is one who has never been baptized. He has come to use the passage!' Then she knocked thrice on the ground with her stick and the ground opened at their feet revealing an incline that led down to the mouth of a passage. Without hesitating, the boy set his foot on the slope and walked down and down, one hand clutching the hilt of his sword. As he disappeared from sight into the passage, the ground closed up again, leaving the wise-woman alone by the foot of the oak.

As the ground closed, shutting out the daylight, the boy saw that the walls of the passage were studded with jewels that suddenly began to sparkle and flash, so that for a moment the boy was dazzled by the brightness and had to stop. Soon, however, his eyes became accustomed to the brilliance and he walked on. The floor of the passage was firm and well-trodden and he made good speed. After a while he came to where a black horse was standing, saddled and bridled, as though waiting for him. It was so beautifully groomed it shone as though it had been polished, and its tail was long and flowing. For a moment the boy was tempted to mount it and ride on, but when he saw that the saddle was Moorish, with high front and high back and studded with jewels, something told him that it would be wiser to trust to his own two legs, so he walked on. As he passed the horse, it vanished. One moment it was there, the next it had gone.

On and on the boy walked, then he came to a river. Just as he reached the bank, a boat came into view. In it were six girls, all as lovely as you could wish. Four were rowing while one sat in the bows and another in the stern. They smiled and beckoned to him and offered to row him across, but the boy thought girls silly and did not want anything to do with them, especially Moorish girls as these obviously were, so he said no thank you and boldly waded into the water. Fortunately the river was not very deep at this point and he passed across safely, holding his sword above his head. As he stepped on to dry land on the opposite side, the boat and the girls in it vanished. One moment they were there, the next they had gone. The boy rubbed his eyes, wondered and walked on, hoping that he would soon reach the end of the passage.

On and on he walked, and then all at once he became aware of a pitiful sound, the sound of someone sobbing. It sounded like a child and reminded the boy so much of his baby sister that he broke into a run. The next moment he saw a little boy of perhaps four years old sitting on the ground sobbing as though his heart was breaking. The boy stopped and asked what was the matter. The child turned up a tear-stained face and said that he was a long long way from home and so tired he could not walk another step and was sure he would never see home again. Would not the boy, he asked, who was big and strong, carry him for a bit, just a little way? The boy felt so sorry for the child that, though he ought to have been suspicious because the child was dressed in Moorish clothes, he never gave the fact a thought, but stooped down and picked the child up. As the child put his thin little arms round the boy's neck, the tiny hands at the end of those slender arms suddenly became the hands of a giant, huge and enormously strong, and they closed on the boy's throat and tried to strangle him. Fortunately for the boy, being unbaptized he could not be killed by Moorish magic, so, after repeated attempts to strangle the boy had failed, the hands relaxed their grip and suddenly they and the child vanished. If it had not been for the soreness of his neck and the livid marks on it left by big strong fingers, the boy might have thought he had dreamed it all. Rubbing his throat, he walked on, wondering what was going to happen to him next.

He had not long to wait. All at once the passage was plunged into darkness, bringing the boy to a halt. For a long time he stood there wondering what to do, then he grinned to himself; he had had an idea. Unsheathing his sword he began striking at the walls. Each time the steel of the sword struck one of the many jewels with which the walls were studded it produced sparks, and there were so many sparks that the boy was able to walk along by their light, hacking at the walls as he went.

His arm began to ache and he was just wondering

how much longer he could go on, when suddenly thousands of lamps lit up and, in the blaze of light, he saw two enormous tigers, which crouched down at the sight of him and began lashing their tails, while their eyes blazed. It seemed to the boy as though they were about to spring at him and tear him to pieces. Now he was really frightened, but he walked on, sword in hand. Closer and closer he went, then all of a sudden the tigers turned and ran off.

The boy had now been walking for two days and nights and he badly wanted to sit down and rest, but he was afraid of falling asleep in such a place where horrible things happened to one, so he decided that he had better press on. So he walked on and on, and when he judged that it must be evening again and he was beginning to feel downhearted, he turned a corner and his heart gave a leap: there was the secret entrance to the Alcazar of the great Al Rachid! He had come to the end of the passage.

The two great gates, which had jewelled hinges and mountings, stood wide open and for an instant the boy thought that he had overcome the last of his obstacles, but the next moment he saw that his way was barred by an enormous frog, so huge it quite filled the gateway. Flames darted from the frog's mouth and its eyes blazed with an evil fire. It was the ugliest and most frightening thing he had ever seen and his heart almost failed him, as he realized that he could not get past. He might even have turned back, only the thought of trying to make his way back the way he had come was almost as frightening as that of having to face the frog. But he had to do something. At last he thought of a trick. Swinging his sword back, he lobbed it over the frog's head, calling out as he did so: 'There! Take that! I'm not afraid of you!'

Hearing the clatter as the sword fell on the ground, the frog turned to see what had caused it, and that gave the boy his opportunity. He took a great leap and landed fair and square on the frog's back. Then, sitting astride the frog, he dug his heels so hard into its sides that the frog gave a loud squawk, leaped round and back through the gateway. As he passed, the boy cleverly snatched up his sword from the ground and used it to hit the frog over the head. The harder he hit, the longer and fiercer were the flames that came from the mouth of the frightened frog, which croaked and grunted most horribly. Altogether there was a dreadful commotion.

. . . dashed back inside the castle.

The noise was so loud that Al Rachid sent a servant to see what it was all about, and when the terrified man told him what he had seen, Al Rachid himself came hurrying out. As he stepped out, the flames from the frog's mouth flickered across him. His long beard caught fire and frizzled up with a great hiss. Flames appeared on the silk of his baggy trousers and on his gold-embroidered jacket. He turned and dashed back inside the castle just as the boy, taking his sword in both hands, brought it down with such force that he cut the great frog's head right off.

The boy felt himself fall with a bump and was aware of a great hush. Slowly he opened his eyes and looked up into a starry sky. Getting to his feet, he found himself standing among rocks beside a wide river. The frog had vanished, the castle had vanished, there was nothing to be seen of the passage or of the Alcazar of Al Rachid, only there standing by herself was a woman, her face alight with joy. Although she was dressed in Moorish clothes, her face was not that of a Moor, and the boy knew that this was Maria, the farmer's daughter.

Together, Maria and the boy made their way out from among the rocks and set off through the night for home on the other side of the forest. As you can imagine there were great celebrations when Maria and her rescuer arrived, and the farmer, being rich, gave the boy a very handsome reward for all that he had done.

ELEVEN

The Archbishop's Mule

BRAGA HAS ALWAYS been a big and a busy town, and has many inns. In the old days, at the time of this story, these inns employed many ostlers to look after the horses and mules of the travellers who stopped there for refreshment or to spend the night. Of these ostlers, none was so merry as a certain Pablo. He was gay and rather happy-go-lucky and, because he did not always work as much as perhaps he ought to have, he was subsequently poor and usually dressed in old rags. But he was always happy and smiling and it was only very occasionally that he worried about being poor or thought of doing anything to improve his lot. One day, when Pablo was seeing to the archbishop's mule, he paused in his grooming to look at its fat sleek flanks and wonderful, expensive harness, and he said quietly to himself:

'Every one used to call my father a donkey and me they call an ass, but I wish to goodness I were the archbishop's mule. Look at the rich clothes he has! Look at the wine and maize bread I have been ordered to give him! No wonder his flanks are so fat and his skin so glossy! What a lovely life he must lead. I wish I were an archbishop's mule.'

At the thought of his being a mule, he leaned back

against the manger and laughed so much that the mule stopped eating and looked up at him.

'Do you mean that?' asked the mule. 'Have you ever seen the archbishop? Do you know how stout he is? Have you any idea what he weighs? A lot, I can tell you. But if you would like to change with me, you're welcome. Just take hold of both my ears and wish, and a mule you shall be. And in the archbishop's service.'

At that the ostler put down his curry-comb, and taking hold of the mule's ears with his two hands said: 'I wish I were the archbishop's mule.' No one, I am sure, could have been more surprised than Pablo, when he suddenly found that he was a mule. Not only that, but where there had been the archbishop's mule, he now saw a monk.

'Come now, monk,' said Pablo. 'Be my ostler. Fetch me my maize bread and wine.'

But the monk just ran out of the stable, not even deigning to look at Pablo, and it was then that poor Pablo realized that he had made a mistake, and he made up his mind that as soon as he was led out into the street, he would run off to his mother and hope she could hide him.

Having had his siesta inside the inn, the archbishop called for his mule. The innkeeper called for Pablo, but no Pablo appeared. In the end, one of the archbishop's own attendants had to go and saddle the archbishop's mule, which he did so badly, that, no sooner were they outside the stable, than the saddle slipped round under the mule's belly and the archbishop's servant let go of the reins to put matters right. That gave Pablo his opportunity and, kicking up his heels, he bolted off down the road in the direction of his mother's house.

The archbishop, who had been standing in the door-
way of the inn and seen all that had happened, thought
that his mule had gone mad and told his other servants
to give chase. Off they ran full pelt and the crowd of
onlookers, thinking it all great fun, joined in the chase.

Pablo never stopped till he reached his mother's
house where, forgetting that he was a mule, he rushed
in. Bending over his mother, who was spinning at her
distaff, he tried to her amazement to kiss her hand.
Then, wanting to explain and ask for her help, he found
that now he was unable to speak. His poor mother was
terrified by this great beast suddenly bursting into her
room, but had presence of mind enough to beat it over
the head with her distaff, exclaiming as she did so:
'Abernuncio!'

By this time the archbishop's servants and the others
had surrounded the old lady's little house. They got
hold of Pablo's bridle and dragged him out, then they
tried to lead him off in the direction of the inn. But
Pablo refused to go. He kicked and reared and even lay
down on his side and rolled in the dust till the archbishop's scarlet saddle-cloth was quite ruined. Then,
suddenly leaping up, he dived back into the cottage and
tried to sit down on his usual chair.

This was too much for his poor mother, who fled
shrieking from the house. The people swarmed in after
Pablo and beat him so hard with their sticks that in the
end he was glad to go back to the inn. After being
groomed to clean off the dust and dirt, he allowed the
archbishop to mount, and off they went. However,
Pablo, not being accustomed to working four legs,
moved his right fore and hind legs together, a most uncomfortable gait that made the poor archbishop, who
was a fat man, roll about in the saddle. The archbishop

grunted and gasped and felt that his mule must be bewitched. Why else should it suddenly have developed the gait of a camel?

Eventually, the poor archbishop became so sore that he could sit no longer, so, laying hold of the pommel in both hands, he stood up in his stirrups. He was then just entering a village and the people, who had all come out of their cottage to gape and goggle at His Eminence, thought he was going to preach a sermon, so they all doffed their caps and knelt down in the dust, expecting the archbishop to bless them.

The way they flopped to their knees looked so funny that Pablo, forgetting he was now a mule, began to splutter and laugh. The villagers, thinking it was the archbishop clearing his throat, did not look up; while the archbishop became seriously afraid that somehow or other his fine mule had been bewitched, and on the principle that it is better to be safe than sorry, he raised his two gloved hands and in solemn tones said:

'Exorciso te – abernuncio!'

This the archbishop ought not to have done, or at least he should have kept one hand on the pommel, because as he heard the dread words, Pablo sat down on his haunches and the poor prelate slid down abruptly and was left lying on the ground, from which position he uttered another wrathful, 'Abernuncio!' in such heartfelt tones that Pablo leaped to his feet, sending the archbishop tumbling head over heels.

The archbishop got to his feet covered in dust, and at the sight of him Pablo was stricken with remorse. Thinking he ought to show his contrition in the usual way – usual that is for a person, though not for a mule – he dropped to his knees (or his fore-legs) and this so startled everybody that most of them took to their heels and rushed back inside their houses. One old woman, however, who understood mules, exclaimed:

'Oh, look! The poor beast's saying it's sorry. It did not mean to upset His Eminence!'

Then Pablo, getting to his feet again, put his foreleg forward and his hind leg back, as he had seen really well-trained mules do, so as to make it easier for the archbishop to mount, and the archbishop who was a kind man at heart and the last person to bear a grudge, got back into the saddle. No sooner did he feel the archbishop's weight on his back than Pablo, being very contrite and wishing to make up for the time that had already been lost through his fault, set off at a quick amble. This was such an uncomfortable pace that the archbishop had to hold on to the crupper with one hand and the pommel with the other, so that the villagers not only did not get their sermon, but were deprived of their blessing and stood watching open-mouthed as their prelate was borne off down the highway with his attendants, who journeyed on foot, toiling along behind and quite unable to keep up. Soon, however, Pablo began to tire and slackened his pace, so that by dint of running the attendants were able to catch up with their master, just as he was reaching the city gate. Then, two of them took Pablo by the bridle, one on each side, and so they reached the city.

There was quite a crowd of priests and townspeople waiting at the city gate to greet His Eminence the Archbishop. When Pablo and his rider were just a few yards away, one of the priests raised a large silver cross aloft. At the sight of this Pablo, again forgetting that he was no longer a human but a mule, dropped to his knees, as he had always been taught to do. This sudden movement pitched the archbishop on to Pablo's neck.

As he overbalanced he clutched at his two attendants. Both happened to have large sticking out ears and it was these the archbishop's hands caught hold of, almost tearing them out by the roots. Not realizing who it was had pulled their ears, the two men began hitting out at all and sundry, but only succeeded in knocking the archbishop down. Seeing this they took to their heels and ran, and Pablo, eager to make amends, galloped after them, his mouth wide open, intending to bite them if he could catch them. The two men, realizing that they were bound to be overtaken, dived into a nearby chapel and banged the door in Pablo's face.

Pablo was so put out by their escape that when he turned and saw people laughing at him, as he thought, he lost his temper and rushed at the crowd. In those days many people used to wear trousers made of leather, but Pablo the mule had a fine set of teeth and in no time at all he had torn great pieces out of four pairs of leather trousers, kicked fifteen people and trampled on scores of others; then, realizing the horrible punishment that was sure to be meted out to him, he rushed off back down the road he had come and never stopped till he reached the inn where he had worked as ostler.

The innkeeper, presuming that the archbishop had met with an accident, led his mule to the stable, groomed it and gave it another feed of wine and maize-bread. As he ate, Pablo wondered what on earth he was going to do. Whatever he may have thought earlier in the dawn, he realized now that he would rather be anything than the archbishop's mule. But who could change him back into Pablo the ostler? The inn's cat leaped through the window on its nightly rat hunt and Pablo asked it if it could help, but the cat just said 'Miaow!' and walked on. Then, just as Pablo was on the point of falling asleep, he heard the creak of the stable door opening and in came the monk, who, before, had been the mule. The monk was not looking at all happy, certainly not as happy as Pablo felt he would have been if only he could have had two legs instead of four.

'Well, Pablo,' said the monk, 'how do you like being a mule?'

Now Pablo was easy-going and good-natured, but he was also astute, and not wanting the monk to know that he had got into trouble, he said:

'Well, I like the smart harness and I suppose I enjoy carrying the archbishop as much as he enjoys being carried, but I am not accustomed to eating such rich fare or so much, and I am afraid it may harm my health.'

'Does that mean that you would rather not be the archbishop's mule?' asked the monk.

'Well,' said Pablo, 'it's certainly a good job, but the most important thing is to be healthy, isn't it?'

'All right,' said the monk, 'let's do another swop. I became the archbishop's mule in order to get away from my wife, but she recognized me even though I was disguised as a monk, so nothing was gained. Good gracious, hurry, I believe I hear her coming.'

Saying that, the monk seized Pablo by his two long ears and gazing at him intently, said:

'I wish I were the archbishop's mule.'

Now the strange thing is that, in the morning, when the innkeeper came to feed the archbishop's mule, the stable was empty except for Pablo, whom he found asleep on the straw, snoring loudly. Fearing that he might be blamed for losing the archbishop's splendid and no doubt most valuable mule, the innkeeper never told anyone how it had come back the previous evening. In fact, he did not even ask Pablo where he had been, but acted as though none of all this had ever happened, but was just a dream. And so, perhaps, it was?

TWELVE

The Great Fish

LONG, LONG AGO there was a poor fisherman who had
three daughters. One day, when he was fishing, his nets
were so heavy that he felt sure he had made an enormous catch and was thrilled with his good luck. But
imagine his disappointment when, on drawing in the
nets, he found not a splendid catch of fish but just one
huge, ugly old fish, which spoke to him in a human
voice, saying: 'Fisherman! Go home and bring your
eldest daughter to me. If you disobey I will punish you
with ill-luck and a life of misery. Now, hurry!'

Trembling with fright the fisherman returned home
and told his eldest daughter about the big fish and its
terrible command. She was a brave girl and loved her
father, and she decided that at all cost he must be
spared, so she got herself ready and went with her father
back to the shore where the great fish waited for
them. The fisherman cried sorrowfully at leaving his
daughter with this ugly monster of the deep, but he
felt himself completely in its power and dared not
disobey.

But, poor man, this was not the end of his troubles.
Each time he cast his fishing nets he hauled in the same
great fish and each time it asked for another of his
daughters, until it had taken away all three. But when

at last it had carried off all the poor man's daughters, it rewarded him with rich presents of jewels and gold, so that the fisherman was poor no longer and he and his wife could live a life of comfort and ease. But they were so sad without their three dear daughters that they had not the heart to enjoy their wealth.

After several years the fisherman and his wife had a baby son. They were overjoyed, for now again they had a child to love and look after, and this comforted them for the loss of the three girls whom they missed so sadly.

The boy grew up happily with his loving parents in their fine house, and when he was a man he was told that once his father had been a poor fisherman and had sold his three daughters for his present wealth.

The young man asked his father if this was true, and the father then told him the whole sad story of the great fish, its threats and demands and finally its rich rewards, when, at last, it had taken the three sisters away. The young man was horrified at the tale and said to his father, 'I cannot bear to think of what may have befallen my sisters. They may be unhappy and cruelly treated. I must find out what has happened to them and, if they are held against their will, I shall try and set them free.'

The father was worried at his son's determination. He was the only child left to comfort his wife and himself in their old age and he was terribly afraid that the young man would fall into the clutches of the huge fish and never be heard of again. But nothing could persuade the son to stay at home, and after saying good-bye to his anxious parents he set out on his great adventure.

He had not travelled far when he came across three boys having a dreadful quarrel and fighting all over the road. He made them stop and then asked them what they had been quarrelling about. They told him that their father had died and left them a pair of boots, a cloak and a key. Whoever owned the boots could be carried by them to wherever he wished as quick as lightning. The cloak would make its owner invisible. And the key would open any lock. The brothers were fighting because they could not agree as to which of them should inherit the boots, the cloak or the key.

When the young man heard this, he realized that these three things could be an enormous help to him in his search for his sisters, so he offered to settle the boys' quarrel by giving them a very large sum of money which they could divide equally among themselves. Being a rich young man he could afford to pay them well and soon he was the owner of the three magic articles, while the three brothers were going on their way, with plenty of money in their pockets, their dispute forgotten.

When they had gone, the young man pulled on the boots and said, 'Boots! Take me to my eldest sister, wherever she may be.' At once the boots whisked him over the sea without wetting his feet, and set him down in a wonderful park, full of shady trees which stretched far along the shore. On the beach there were thousands of prettily coloured little sea-creatures, which flashed and twinkled in the sun. The rippling waves splashed and broke into shining drops on the sand and even the air seemed clearer and more sparkling – magic air, to be breathed by nymphs and mermaids.

In the middle of the park stood a magnificent gleaming palace, surrounded by gardens. They were as colourful as any earthly gardens, but filled with seaweed of every imaginable colour. Pink, silver, scarlet, orange, green and gold, they spread their feathery fronds and crisp leaves amongst branches of white and rose-coloured coral. There were pillars of shells and mother-of-pearl and the young man gazed with delight at the strange and beautiful scene.

And then he noticed a beautifully dressed lady, who looked like a queen, walking in the garden surrounded by her ladies-in-waiting. She had also seen him, and though greatly surprised at seeing a stranger in her garden she came towards him graciously and asked him how he had found his way to her palace and what business brought him there.

He looked her straight in the eyes and answered gravely, 'I am your brother.'

'But I have no brother,' the lady replied, and so the young man told her the story of her father and the fish and explained why he had come here, to find out what fate had befallen his eldest sister.

The queen was overjoyed to see her brother, whom she hadn't even known about before, and she embraced him and invited him in to the palace. As they went inside she hesitated a moment and said, 'I must tell you that my husband is a great and powerful king of the Fishes. Although he is devoted to me and treats me very kindly, he is most terribly jealous. I am afraid he may be furiously angry to find you here when he returns, and he may even try to kill you.'

'Do not worry,' said the young man. 'I have the good fortune to own a magic cloak which makes me invisible when I put it on. I shall wear it when your husband returns and he won't ever suspect that I am here.'

So the queen was reassured, and she led her brother through many rooms of her wonderful palace. There were great halls supported by pillars which were stalactites and stalagmites soaring to the roof that shone and glimmered with a pearly light high above them. In some of the rooms the walls were panelled with mother-of-pearl; some were covered with coral and others with transparent fish scales which twinkled and sparkled wherever the light struck them. The archways and doorways were made of great curving branches of coral, while the furniture was inlaid with pearls and exquisite rose-tinted shells.

The young man had never seen anything so gorgeous and beautiful. Or so strange.

All at once there was a roaring, rushing sound, and the Great King of the Fishes approached, fierce eyes gleaming and a sinister rumbling coming from his throat. The queen hurried to meet him and gave him a fond welcome. She led him to his marble throne, and while he rested she talked to him gently and soothingly. When he seemed to be in a better temper she said, 'Dear husband, I have great news to tell you.'

'And who has been here to bring you news?' rumbled the Fish King.

'Great king and dear husband,' the queen gently murmured, 'it is only my own brother, whom I have never seen until today, who has come to visit us. I feared you might harm him and I bade him hide until I had told you about his presence here.'

The great fish rumbled a bit more, but seeing the pleading look in his wife's eyes, he said, 'Bring him to me. I will receive him.' Then, seeing her hesitate, he continued, 'do not fear, I give you my word that I will not harm him.'

So the queen brought her brother to the king, who was very kind and gracious to him. They talked together and then the king told the young man that if ever he should find himself in a difficult situation and in need of help, he need only say 'Come to my aid, King of the Fishes,' and in a flash he would be beside him and give him whatever assistance he needed. The king then gave the young man a present of gold and silver, after which he and the queen embraced him and he left. He went on his way very gratified to have found his sister and to know that she was happy and well treated in the marvellous palace of the King of the Fishes.

Once again he put on his magic boots and said, 'Boots! Take me to my second sister. Wherever she may be!' and this time he was immediately whisked across great mountain ranges, above dizzy gorges and precipices and at last across a wide bay, where the water was calm and as clear and green as glass. In the middle of the bay was an island, its sides rising sheer out of the water, and it was plain to see that no one could ever land there from the sea, but the magic boots set the young man down on the middle of the island. He followed a path which led him to the entrance of a great cave. In the distance he could hear the sound of an organ playing and the solemn music rolled and echoed round the cave. He stepped inside and was met by an attendant who asked him his business. The young man replied that he had come to visit his sister who lived there and the attendant requested him to wait while he took the message. While he waited, the young man gazed in wonder at the walls of the cave, which were covered in white and orange sponges. Between them grew sea-anemones of every kind; mauve, pink, green and purple. The colours were dazzling and the young man was marvelling at it all, when the attendant returned and said that he would conduct him to the queen. 'But,' he added, 'she has only agreed to see you because she knows that some fairy or mermaid has brought you here, since no mortal man can land on the island. She desires me to tell you that she has no brother.'

The young man followed the attendant who threw open two great gates of silver and led him into a huge room lined with jade and amethyst. The queen was sitting on a throne carved from crystal and rose quartz, and her robes were made of finest seaweed, like lace of delicate green and white threads. All round her throne sat beautiful mermaids, who were her ladies-in-waiting.

In the middle of the

The queen asked the young man to state his reason for coming to the island and he replied that it was because of his desire to know of her fate after their father had sold her to the King of the Fishes.

'But I have no brother,' the queen replied.

'I was born a few years after you left home,' said the young man, 'and when I learned of the reason for your going, I could not rest until I found you and knew if you were happy and well treated.'

At these words the queen embraced her brother and thanked him for his concern. But she warned him that her husband was the King of Seals, kind and loving to her, but furiously resentful of strangers, and she said she dared not introduce them until she had put her husband in a good temper, when he returned home, as he usually arrived tired and cross from settling

bay was an island.

the disputes of his subjects, who were very quarrel-some.

The young man told her of his invisible cloak and shortly after, when they heard roars and snarls echoing through the cave, he put it on just as the King of Seals entered the throne room. In a short while the queen had soothed and pacified her strange master and introduced her brother to him. He was kind and courteous and invited the young man to stay with them, so that he could show him all the marvels of his kingdom. The young man thanked him for his invitation, but said that he must not delay finding his youngest sister. Before he left the king gave him a royal sturgeon as food for his journey, and the promise that he would help him at any time of danger or difficulty, if he repeated the words: 'Come to my aid, King of the Seals!'

So the young man bade farewell to his sister and her husband and left the palace. Outside, he requested his magic boots to take him to his youngest sister, and he was soon in a kingdom very different to that of the other two. This was the kingdom of birds and all round him was a magic forest, where tall trees cast a dappled shade on the ground, which was carpeted with beautiful, sweet-scented flowers and delicious little berries of every shade of yellow, red and purple. There were sunny glades, through which a little stream hurried over rocks and splashed into shallow pools where scores of birds fluttered and bathed, while above them the air was filled with whistling and singing as birds flew from tree to tree, making their nests and feeding their young. As the young man wandered on, he saw lakes where ducks and all sorts of water fowl dabbled amongst the reeds, and the trees were loaded with ripe fruit on which many of the birds fed, while others picked up grubs and insects from the ground, which seemed to hold an endless supply of food. At last he came to a grove where several huge trees grew round in a circle. The circle of trees was covered in a mantle of creeper which was aflame with blossoms and formed an enclosure which was the palace of the King of the Birds. At the entrance the young man was met by an attendant whom he asked to conduct him to his sister, the queen. The attendant led him through this strange leafy palace, whose rooms were divided by screens of creepers, all covered with exquisite flowers, glowing with colour and filling the air with a dewy, luscious scent. The soft green light filtering through all the leaves gave a magic quality to the scene and the young man eagerly drank in the beauty and scents of his surroundings. When he came to his sister she, too, had no knowledge of having a brother and indeed, she could hardly remember her parents and sisters, for she had been so young when she left home. But she greeted him affectionately and was eager for news of her family. When the King of the Birds arrived, the air was filled with the rushing of great wings. He welcomed his wife's brother and entertained him lavishly, and when he left gave him a beautiful glittering feather from his wing, saying, 'If you are in danger or trouble repeat "Come to my aid, King of the Birds!" I will at once fly to your assistance.' The young man was delighted with his visit and the welcome given him and he set out for home with his mind at rest, for he had found all three of his sisters and knew that they were happy.

As soon as he had left the forest he saw a great, gloomy-looking tower. It filled him with curiosity and when he asked an old woman, who was passing by, who lived there, she replied,

'Sir, that tower thou lookest on
Is the great tower of Babylon.
Forever shall he rue the hour
Who sets his foot inside that tower.'

This strange warning made the young man more
curious than ever and he determined to explore the
tower, trusting that his magic possessions would protect
him from harm. He put on his boots and told them to
take him inside the tower and at once the huge gates
opened as he was set down inside. It was gloomy and
dark, but as he went from room to room he found that
many of them were richly furnished and others filled
with treasure chests, stuffed with gold and jewels. He
caught sight of a beautiful maiden hurrying along a corridor and he hastened to speak to her. She was so pale
and delicate, like a fragile flower, that he was afraid of
startling her, but he gently asked who she was and how
she came to be in such a sad, forbidding place. She
glanced round timidly before telling him that she had
been kept enchanted in this prison-like tower ever since
she was a baby. Her only companion and the one who
had her in his power was a sickly old man, who was
forever complaining and grumbling. He sighed and
groaned and she felt pity for him as he seemed so
desperate and miserable, but he also filled her with
horror, and her joy at seeing another human soul in
this desolate prison gave her hope and courage. She
begged the young man not to leave her, but to try and
help her escape. He was greatly touched by her story
and her youthful beauty and promised to stay and help
her. Obviously, her release could only be secured
through the old man, so he asked her to go in search of
him.

They found him in the highest room in the tower, wailing and sighing and the girl went up to him and said: 'Tell me why you groan and sigh. Perhaps I could help.' The old man sobbed at her kind words and said, 'I have never dared ask you, but since you have shown an interest in me, I will tell you. At the bottom of the sea there is a huge chest which is the cause of all my trouble. Inside the chest there is a fish, inside the fish there is a seal, inside the seal there is a bird and inside the bird is an egg. If ever anyone found that egg and broke it on my head, I should die. If one day someone had the power to open the chest and its contents, they could finish me off, and the thought of that fills me with anxiety and dread.'

The girl did not tell the old man that there was a stranger in the tower, who possessed magic powers, but just talked soothingly to the old man. Then she hurried back to the young man and told him all she had just learned. He at once resolved to find that mysterious chest, which he was sure could be done with the help of the three kings who were his sisters' husbands. Almost as soon as he had spoken the magic words they appeared and, when they learned what was needed, dived to the bottom of the sea, fished up the mighty chest and delivered it to the young man. He fitted his magic key into the lock, and at once it opened, revealing all the contents that the old man had described. When at last the young man held the egg in his hands he hurried to the top of the tower and broke it over the old man's head. The shrieks that he uttered were horrible indeed, but when they stopped and he lay dead, the beautiful maiden was free at last from her evil enchantment. Hand-in-hand with her rescuer, she left the tower and travelled with him back to his home.

His parents were overjoyed to see him safe and sound. He told them all about his three sisters and the wonderful palaces they lived in, and how they were happy and contented. He and the young girl he had rescued decided to marry, which they did as soon as they could and, I am glad to say, they enjoyed a happy and prosperous life together.

THIRTEEN

The Bashful Prince

ONCE THERE WAS a king in the fair land of Portugal who had only one child, a daughter. Unfortunately, her body was deformed and her face so ugly that when she rode through the streets the children fled in terror thinking she must be a witch. Her father, however, loved her so much that he could see no fault in her; in fact, he thought she was lovely, and because he thought that, the courtiers all said the same and never tired of telling the girl how beautiful she was, so that she really believed that she was.

When the princess grew up, her father arranged for a prince from a distant country to marry his daughter, so the princess had a lovely time ordering her trousseau and helping with the arrangements for her wedding. The dresses were very gorgeous and magnificent and only made the poor girl look uglier, but of course nobody told her so.

The day came when the prince, who was to marry the girl, was due to arrive. The houses were festooned with flags and bunting and the streets were lined with crowds of people all anxious to see the young prince. There were bands playing and in the main square in front of the city a pavilion had been set up with a splendid throne for the king and smaller, though almost

equally splendid ones, for the princess and the prince.
There the king and his daughter waited in state, surrounded by an escort of cavalry; dark-skinned warriors
armed to the teeth, wearing uniforms of white and gold
and mounted on the finest Arab horses obtainable.
Behind the king stood his courtiers and the royal barber
with his retinue of apprentices, while on the right stood
a gigantic negro with an enormous axe over one
shoulder. This was Nabo, the king's executioner, with
the implement of his office. In front of the pavilion, on
either side of the steps leading to the thrones, was a
guard of honour mounted by foot soldiers. These were
dressed in short tunics, like vests, called aljubas, and
wide trousers, and they had richly ornamented quivers
full of arrows with gaily coloured feathers.

From his throne the king could see down the street to
the ancient bridge that carried the highway across the
river, and on this now appeared a cavalcade of such
size that he knew the prince must be approaching.

The prince, who was a nice young man and a dutiful
son, had agreed to marry the princess because his father
had told him it would be good for the country if he did
so; and, as he wasn't in love with anyone else, he thought
that he might as well do as his father wished. Reaching
the front of the pavilion the prince dismounted, flinging
the reins of his Arab to one of his pages; then he began
to mount the steps that led up to the three thrones. As
he reached the top step but one his gaze met that of the
king, to whom he smiled. Then his gaze travelled on and,
for the first time, he saw the princess, the girl he was to
marry, and his cheeks paled as he paused, left foot on
the top step. But he could not stop there, and had to
continue, so going up to the king he saluted him deferen-
tially; but he found that he just could not bring himself

to look at the princess, let alone kiss her cheek, as she would expect the man she was to marry to do.

Turning to the king, the young prince said:

'Sire! You must excuse my bashfulness; but the fact is that Princess Altamira is so much more beautiful than I was led to expect, so transcendently beautiful, in fact, that if I look at her face again, I cannot expect to live.'

The king, and the princess, were highly flattered. The king invited the prince to take his seat at the princess's side but the prince refused, pleading his insuperable bashfulness and the dangers he was sure he would incur by being near or looking at the princess. The king insisted, the prince refused, politely but firmly; then the king began to get angry and said:

'Prince Alanbam! We fully appreciate the motives that prompt this conduct, but you must remember that you have come here to wed the Princess Altamira, who as a Christian king and the first of my line, I intend to lead to the altar. You are her affianced husband, Prince Alanbam.'

The prince paled again and there was a slight quaver of apprehension in his voice, as he replied:

'Sire,' he said, 'that cannot be. I would rather marry someone less beautiful. Forgive me if I disappoint you, but I cannot be wedded to so much beauty.'

The king was all but speechless with rage. The princess, feeling both flattered and angry, and thinking that she would spite the prince, said:

'With your permission, my royal Father, since I am too beautiful for a prince, I shall marry a man of learning. Who is the most learned man in your kingdom?'

'Bernardo, our royal barber,' the king answered. 'Certainly you shall marry him.' And, turning round, he called:

H

'Bernardo, come here!'

But Bernardo's knees were knocking together in fear and he was trembling so that he could not move. His lips moved, but not a sound came out.

'What's wrong with you, Bernardo?' the king asked angrily. 'Come here man!'

'My royal Master,' stammered the poor barber, 'I can no more avail myself of this wonderful honour than could the Archbishop. His Grace is bound to celibacy, and I am already married.'

Now the barber was really quite a good man, but he had made an enemy of one of the courtiers, who, seeing how the king was perplexed and at a loss and seeing a chance to get his own back on the barber, said:

'Sire, your people, I am sure, would be delighted to see beauty wedded to learning in this union you propose. Our good friend Bernardo was married, it is true; but since he has been at court he has fallen in love with Princess Altamira and no longer pays any attention to his wife. Do you, therefore, graciously dissolve his first marriage and so let him marry your dear daughter.'

At this the barber became so furious that he pulled out a razor and rushed at the courtier and would have cut his throat if some of the guards had not caught hold of him and stopped him. They flung the wretched Bernardo to the ground and held him there. The king, without even turning his head, called out in an awe-inspiring voice:

'Nabo! Do your duty!'

The royal executioner stepped forward. His strong black arms raised the gleaming headman's axe aloft and at one stroke Bernardo's head was severed from his body.

Prince Alanbam realized that with the king in this

mood he might himself be the next victim; so, stepping forward, he said:

'Sire, I have a suggestion. Let one hundred knights be chosen and let them fight for the honour of the princess's hand. I myself will enter the lists. The survivor shall be rewarded by marrying your daughter.'

'An excellent idea,' said the king, his face brightening. And then he called out ninety-nine of his best knights and told them that they were to enter the lists. 'And fight valiantly,' he said, 'because the reward is great and precious.'

So the ninety-nine knights and the prince withdrew to put on their armour, and soon two lots of fifty knights on beautiful chargers stood facing each other from opposite ends of the list. The king gave the signal and the knights charged at each other. The horses galloped faster and faster; the two sets of knights met in a flurry of dust, but to the astonishment of the spectators and the chagrin of the king, no one was wounded, no one unhorsed. In fact, it almost looked as if they had all done their best to expose themselves without making any attempt to fight.

Again the knights assembled at opposite ends of the lists, and again they charged down on each other with exactly the same results. When, at the end of the fourth charge, no one had yet even suffered a scratch, much less been unseated, the king scowled and announced that he was changing the rules of the contest. 'From now on,' he said, 'the knight who is first wounded shall be the winner and marry my daughter.'

The fifth charge resulted in a fearful mêlée. The knights fought like wild-cats, each trying his utmost to inflict a wound, before himself being wounded. In the end, every knight was wounded and most had been unhorsed, but they were quite unable to agree as to whom had been wounded first. Then, feeling desperate, the king announced that he thought his daughter had best be married to the church and so would enter a convent, so that her transcendent beauty would cause no more trouble.

'No, father,' said the Princess, 'I shall get myself a husband. If there is no one worthy of me in this fair land of Portugal, I will leave it for ever. In the north is a country where day never dawns and night is eternal. I shall go there, because all degrees of beauty must be equal, and I know now that it is just as unfortunate to be too beautiful as to be very ugly.'

So Princess Altamira said good-bye to her father and was just walking away when a young fiddler, who was both handsome and blind, thrust his way through the throng and called out:

'Wait! Princess, you have no need to go North to find one to whom all degrees of beauty are equal. In me you behold one to whom night and day, extreme ugliness and transcendent beauty, are the same. If everyone who can see is too modest and bashful to marry you, allow me to offer myself as your husband. In my world "handsome is as handsome does".'

The king was so pleased with the suggestion that meant that his daughter would not need to go away, that he at once made Felisberto – that was the blind fiddler's name – a count, endowed him with estates suited to his new position, and pronounced him his son-in-law to be.

Now you might think that such an oddly assorted couple would not be happy. But the fact is that the princess was really a nice person and now that her foolish illusion had been shattered, she was determined to make a success of her marriage; and because Felisberto had a heart-of-gold and the character to enable him to triumph over his blindness, they were very happy together.

FOURTEEN

Kernel

MANY YEARS AGO there lived two Portuguese peasants who, though they had been married several years, had no children. Although they were poor and had to work very hard to make a living out of their stony little patch of ground, they would have been perfectly happy and contented if only they could have had a child. Their cottage was so quiet and still when they returned to it after the day's work and, when they stopped to rest beneath the shady branches of a chestnut tree in the heat of mid-day, they longed to have a hot and grubby baby with whom to share a refreshing drink of goat's milk, a little child, for whom they could spread a cloak under the tree and watch over it as it slept.

One day, as they were eating their simple meal in the shade, an old woman came slowly and painfully towards them begging them for something to eat, and, poor though they were, the good-natured peasants gave her a piece of bread, some figs wrapped in a leaf and a drink of milk from their goat-skin bag. The old woman thanked them for their generosity and asked them what they most desired in all the world. The peasant woman sadly replied 'that which I can never have, a child to love and look after.'

'And I say that your wish shall be granted,' said the

old woman, handing back the leaf in which the figs had been wrapped, and there kicking and chuckling in the middle of the leaf lay the sweetest and tiniest baby boy you have ever seen. When the two peasant lifted their enraptured eyes from the baby, the old woman had vanished and then, of course, they knew that she had been a good fairy and not an old woman at all.

With infinite care and tenderness they carried their tiny treasure back to the cottage and set him down on a table wrapped in his leaf. He was merry and strong, for all his miniature size. 'He's no bigger than a kernel of maize,' breathed the peasant woman softly. 'Let us call him "Kernel"!' said her husband with a chuckle, and she nodded very gently, her heart brimming with a new happiness.

The little boy grew no bigger than an inch high, but it was quite obvious that he was a fairy child because he was every bit as strong as any sturdy little boy and he loved to take his father's breakfast out to the fields where he had been at work from early morning. Kernel would balance the basket on his head and with his enormous load go hopping over the rough ground, so that anyone seeing it must have thought the basket bewitched, jogging along on its own like that.

His parents were amused by his quaint ways, laughing at the mischievous tricks he got up to and adoring him altogether, but they were constantly afraid that some accident might happen to him, because he was so tiny and so bold and venturesome. His father particularly warned him to keep out of the oxen's way, in case they trampled him or lay down on him; but one day when he had taken breakfast to his father he climbed up a stalk of maize that grew in the field and with a long piece of grass tickled the nose of one of the oxen that were standing yoked together, dozing in the sun. They lifted their slow heads and the nearest one wrapped its long tongue round the piece of grass and drew it into its mouth – and swallowed. Little Kernel was still clinging to the grass stem as he disappeared down the ox's throat and his father heard his shouts and hurried to the spot too late. He could still hear the little fellow shouting faintly from inside the ox and he rushed home to his wife to tell her the sad tale and to ask her what they could do. 'You must kill the ox,' she said firmly. 'For though we may be poor and the ox is part of our livelihood, yet there are no riches in the world that are worth the life of our little son.' So the peasant killed his ox and cut it open, but he could find no trace of the tiny boy and he returned home to his wife weeping and with all hope gone.

In the night a wolf came sneaking round the fields, attracted by the smell of the ox meat, and finding the carcass it ate a good meal. Suddenly Kernel, who had been asleep inside the ox, woke up in the wolf's stomach and started to kick and shout. The wolf was terrified of a human voice and fled from the farm, thinking it was being pursued, and after a while Kernel's vicious kicks and struggles were so upsetting to the wolf's digestion that the wretched animal was violently sick and slunk away, leaving Kernel lying on the ground, rather dazed but unhurt. He picked himself up and set out to look for a puddle in which he could have a good wash. When he found one he undressed, had a bath and then washed out his clothes and hung them on a thistle to dry. Then he lay down in the sun for a rest and, when his clothes had dried, he put them on and set off for home.

He had not gone far, when he met a party of mule drovers travelling along the road in his direction. He wished them 'Good day' and asked if he could ride on the back of one of their mules. They were much astonished and amused by the tiny man and his cheery manner, so they picked him up and popped him on one of the panniers that the mules carried and which, he soon discovered, were loaded with bags of money.

He lay down in the sun.

As they journeyed along they were waylaid by a band of robbers who were hiding behind some rocks. They sprang out on the mule drovers and after a fierce struggle overpowered them and left them lying dead and wounded in the dust. Then they seized the mules by their bridles and whacked them into a trot in the direction of a thick forest where the brigands had their hiding place. In the midst of this dark forest was an empty mansion, which was the brigands' hide-out. They unlocked the gate with a great iron key and it creaked back on rusty hinges. They hustled the scared mules into a grim stone courtyard and there unloaded the bags of money.

All this time Kernel had lain hidden in the fold of a money bag, into which he had slipped to hide when the skirmish began, and he was carried into the gloomy house. Through large, shabby rooms and damp, echoing corridors they went and finally a large door was unlocked and he was flung roughly down on to a table on which the robbers began emptying out the money bags in order to count the treasure. Kernel whisked down the table leg and hid beneath it and then shouted at the top of his voice, 'Stop thief! Stop thief!'

The brigands dropped their spoil with a clatter, looked round wildly, drew their knives and fled, thinking they were discovered.

Little Kernel spluttered with laughter to see the band of robbers fly in disorder for fear of him, and he calmly set about collecting the money into the bags. Then he carried them out to the courtyard, where he found the mules and spoke to them in a soothing voice, loaded their panniers with the money bags and set off for his home, driving the train of mules ahead of him.

He arrived at his home while it was still dark, and halting the mules in front of his parents' cottage he kicked and banged on the door. His father, hearing the clatter, looked out of the window and called 'Who's there?'

Kernel shouted back, 'It is I, your son, dear father! Come down and let me in!'

The peasant and his wife were overjoyed. They rushed downstairs and threw open the door and there stood their beloved little son, as perky and cheeky as you please.

Then, over a meal of hot soup and bread, Kernel told his parents about all his adventures since he had last seen them. He gave them the mules and the bags of money, which brought them so much wealth that they were poor no longer and never needed to work again, but were able to buy a fine house where they and their tiny son lived in peace and prosperity.

FIFTEEN

An Expensive Omelette

ONCE THERE WAS a young man who left home with very little money in his pocket to seek his fortune in distant lands. Where he came from and where he was heading for the story does not relate, but one day at noon he came to a little inn near the town of Castello Branco and asked the landlady if he could have something to eat. The woman could offer nothing but eggs so the young man, being hungry, asked her to make him an omelette with six eggs. Having finished his meal the young man produced a gold coin, his only one left, to pay for it, but the woman had no change and, as the eggs only cost a farthing, she said that the young man need not bother, he could pay her next time he passed by.

So the young man went on his way. He came to Lisbon and joined a ship sailing for the distant lands of China, and there he made a fortune trading in silks and tea and jade. After twelve years he returned to Portugal and, leaving most of his goods and valuables with a friend there, set off home to see if any of his family were still alive.

On his way he passed through the same village where he had eaten the six-egg omelette, and remembering that he owed the landlady a farthing, he stopped at the inn and went in to pay his debt. At first the woman did not recognize him, but when he told her who he was, she remembered. Now the landlady was a cunning and a greedy woman, and, seeing how prosperous the man now looked, she said:

'You can't discharge that debt with just a farthing. Let me make out your true bill. Six eggs would have hatched into six hens, they could have laid 72 eggs that would have hatched into 72 hens that would have laid 12 eggs each that would have hatched in to as many hens . . .' and so the woman went till she had worked out a bill as long as a greyhound's tail, which made out that the man owed her 20,631 ducats, which was much more money than he had on him. As he was both unable to pay and disputed the correctness of her bill, the woman pretended to fly into a temper and sent for the policeman. Hearing her story, the policeman arrested the man and put him in prison.

When the day came for the man to be tried he was led into court and there, to his surprise, a young man came up to him and said:

'Sir, I am a student of law. You have no one to defend you, so let me plead your cause. It will be good practice for me.'

The man was only too glad to agree. When the case opened the young student stood up and asked for a brief adjournment in order to have time to consult with his client. The magistrate asked why he had not consulted with his client before, since the man had been in prison for over a week. The student replied:

'Sir, I have been summoned in haste to take on this case and could not come before, as I was in the chestnut wood roasting chestnuts for seed.'

Hearing this, the landlady snorted disdainfully and exclaimed aloud:

'What a fool! Will chestnut trees grow from roasted chestnuts?'

The student turned to her, finger pointing accusingly and said:

'No, Madame, nor can chickens be hatched from fried eggs. Thus this man owes you nothing but the farthing he has offered you.'

The magistrate agreed and dismissed the case. The merchant gave the student a rich reward for his cleverness, while the landlady acquired such a reputation for meanness and dishonesty that people stopped going to her inn and she died in poverty.

SIXTEEN

The Innkeeper's Daughter

ONCE UPON A TIME there was a very beautiful woman who kept a country inn. The inn was on a road along which many merchants and mule drivers used to pass, and many of them stopped at the inn for refreshment or to spend the night.

The beautiful landlady had a daughter who was even fairer than herself, but instead of being fond and proud of her lovely daughter, the mother was furiously jealous of her and angered by the thought that there should be anyone who might attract more admiration than she. Determined that she should keep her reputation of being the best-looking woman for miles around, she hid her daughter in a dark room, behind shuttered windows and a locked door. The poor girl wished with all her heart that she had been born plain or downright ugly, so that she could have helped with the work of the inn and enjoyed the sunshine and the winds that blew from the sierra and all the sights and scents of the countryside, as well as the companionship of her fellows, rather than waste her life away in the solitude of her dark prison.

One day, in a mood of utter despair, the girl managed to force open the shutters and look out of the window on to the world of brightness below her, the sounds from which had for so long delighted and tormented her with their promise of movement and colour. A young mule driver who was pausing for refreshment at the inn happened to look up at the window and saw the face of the girl looking down. She was more beautiful than anything he had ever imagined or seen before.

Downstairs in the inn, the handsome landlady used to ask every traveller if they had ever seen anyone more beautiful than she. And, because she was indeed very fair, they could truthfully satisfy her vanity by saying 'No'. This day, however, when she asked the mule driver the same question, he replied that he had just seen a girl at the window who was far more beautiful than the landlady. The woman caught her breath with rage and whispered to herself.

'How dare she try to look out of the window. But it shan't happen again, for I shall have her killed for this.'

The wicked woman bribed two men to take her daughter to a wild and lonely mountain a few miles away and murder her there. On the journey, the unfortunate girl was so shaken with terror at her terrible fate that she was unable to enjoy the sweet country breeze that stirred her silky hair or the warm sun that fell on her pale and perfectly modelled face for the first time. Her legs felt like stone and she was exhausted with fright and the unaccustomed exercise.

As they came near to the mountain the two rough men almost had to drag the girl along until they came to the top of the mountain. Here they paused, and one of them forced the girl to her knees, while the other raised his axe to cut off her head.

Horror and fear so strangled her that she was unable to utter a word to beg for mercy, but she clasped her hands in an attitude of such pitiful despair, and her eyes were so beautiful with appeal and unshed tears, that the men were suddenly appalled at what they were about to do, the one threw down his axe, and together they raised her to her feet. The other man said:

'We have not the heart to kill you. You must escape and go far from this country, for if your mother ever hears that you are still alive she will punish us severely.'

'Oh, thank you for your mercy,' whispered the girl. 'One day, I hope I may be able to reward you for the kindness you have shown me.'

As soon as the men had gone, the girl followed a twisty stony path down the other side of the mountain and at its foot she came to a gently flowing stream, where she paused to drink and bathe her face and aching feet. The clean cold water felt so wonderful to her skin, alive and invigorating after the water she had known before which was always contained in a chipped and stained jug. Much refreshed, she followed the stream for several miles until she caught sight of a house standing amongst some trees. Darkness was now closing in and the tired and lonely girl went cautiously towards the house. The door stood open and she walked hesitantly in to the great empty hall. She called out, 'Is there any-one here who will give a poor stranger shelter for the night?' Her voice echoed round the empty walls, but there came no answer. With thumping heart she walked in further and went from room to room and along dark corridors, but nowhere could she find a sign of life except for a few pieces of shabby, broken furniture.

Frightening and inhospitable though this great empty mansion would seem to most of us, to the poor girl, freed from her dark room and so recently spared from the threat of death, it seemed as good a place as any in which to shelter for the night. She was very hungry and after a long search found the kitchen. Poking about on the shelves and in the cupboards she encountered rubbish and broken crockery everywhere. At last she found some flour and a little rancid oil and by now she was so famished that these seemed to her to have the makings of a feast. She hurried out into the garden and found some twigs by the light of a moon which shone through tatters in the clouds. She made a fire and in the hot ash baked a flat cake of flour mixed with oil. She had just set this on the kitchen table with a few radishes she had found in the garden and a cupful of water from the well, when she heard noises that so frightened her that she flew to hide, leaving her meagre supper untouched on the table.

The girl timidly

A band of robbers had returned to the empty house, where they came to hide their loot. They saw the little supper on the table and shouted out, 'Hallo there! Who has been here to prepare this supper? Come on out you and show yourself. Or you'll be sorry.'

The girl timidly crept out of her hiding place and stood before the band of robbers afraid that she was again in danger of losing her life.

The men were so amazed at the delicacy of her lovely figure and the beauty of the startled face that looked up at them through the glorious tumble of her hair that their rough words and gestures were hushed and they stared at her with something like reverence in their gaze.

crept out.

They asked her how she had come to this place and why she was all alone. And so the girl told them the whole story of her sad life, her escape from death and her journey to this large deserted house. The men were filled with pity and told her that she could stay with them and that they would protect her and treat her as their sister.

The poor girl was grateful for their offer and so she settled down in the great mansion and kept house for the band of robbers. She cooked their meals and swept and tidied the bare rooms, making them more cheerful with decorations of leaves and flowers which she tended in the rambling overgrown garden.

She was always so sweet and good that her strange, lawless companions were gentle in her presence and provided her with as many comforts as they could afford.

During all this time the girl's wicked mother was continually worrying in case there was someone more beautiful than she. An old woman used to stay at her inn who travelled about a lot carrying messages and running errands for other people, so the landlady never failed to ask her if, on her many travels, she had ever met another woman more beautiful than herself.

'Ah madam,' mumbled the old woman. 'You are indeed beautiful, but not long ago, near the town of Tras-os-Montes, I came across a girl who was more beautiful than anyone I have set eyes on before. Her face and figure were perfection and her little feet! They were the smallest, sweetest feet I have ever seen!'

'This is most interesting,' said the landlady, trying to control the rage that nearly choked her. 'For that lovely girl can be none other than my own lost daughter. Please, I beg of you, the first time that you go that way again, take this present to her from her loving mother.'

She went to a cupboard and took out a pretty little pair of slippers. Handing them to the old woman she said:

'Give these slippers to her with my love and insist that she puts them on before you go. This is very important, as I must know if they still fit her. Do this for me and I will give you a rich reward.'

The old woman was glad to do this simple errand, so she made her way to the house where the girl lived and found her picking flowers in the garden.

'Good morning, little one,' called the old woman. 'I have a present for you here. A present from your loving mother of a pretty pair of shoes.'

The girl looked puzzled. 'But I don't need any shoes,' she replied. 'My brothers give me all the clothes and things that I need. Please take them back to my mother and say that I don't want them.'

The old woman was annoyed that the gift was refused and saw the promised reward slipping from her fingers, so she teased the girl and called her proud and ungrateful and said surely she would be civil enough to try the slippers on just to see if they would fit. The poor girl thought it would be quickest in the end if she tried the slippers on just to get rid of the bothersome old woman, so she put on one shoe and at once one of her eyes closed up. She put on the other and immediately her other eye closed and she fell to the ground dead. The old woman was so startled by this unexpected tragedy that she took to her heels and ran as far from the house as she could.

When the robbers came home that evening they found their beloved little sister lying dead. They were

filled with sadness and could find no explanation for her
sudden death. They could not bear to bury her underneath the dark earth, so they had a glass coffin made
and put her body in it and set it on a hill-top, so that all
who came that way should see how beautiful she was.

It happened that the next day the king's son and
his party of noblemen were returning from a hunt
and passed by the glass coffin. They were surprised
to see it in such an unusual place and the prince
peered through the glass lid and was at once enchanted
by the beauty of the girl lying there. He gazed at her
lovely face, her long dark lashes, her shining hair, and
he marvelled at the delicate smallness of her little hands
and feet. He stood looking at her, wishing with all his
might that a fairy or a magician could bring her back
to life, so that he could make her his bride. After several
minutes, realizing that his courtiers were waiting for
him, he turned to go; but at the last moment he felt he
must have something belonging to this beautiful girl
that he could keep for ever. Carefully raising the lid of
the coffin he drew one of the pretty slippers from her
foot. At once she opened an eye. And now the prince,
filled with amazement and hope, eagerly pulled the
second slipper from her foot. She opened her other eye
and, before the young man's delighted gaze, the
beautiful girl came to life. He clasped her little hands
and helped her from the coffin. She stood there, sweeter
and prettier than any girl he had ever seen.

The prince sent one of his courtiers hurrying back to
the palace to send a carriage for them and to tell the
king and his court of their arrival. And everyone at the
palace fell under the spell of the girl's beauty and character and were shocked by the story of her hard life and
of her wicked mother. Within a few weeks the prince

and the girl were married and everyone rejoiced and wished them happiness.

A little later the prince took his bride to her mother's inn. He insisted on showing the woman that her cruel plans had failed and that her daughter, by her beauty and sweetness, had won the heart of the king's own son. Nothing could harm her now that she was under his protection and her bad mother was so consumed with jealousy when she saw the good fortune that had come to her daughter, that lines and wrinkles of temper and despair ravaged her face, so that in a short while no one would have guessed that she had ever been good-looking.

But the prince and his princess lived happily in their palace, showing nothing but kindness to their people and their family of pretty children.

SEVENTEEN

The One-legged Chicken

LONG AGO, in a little village in Portugal, there lived a priest who kept an old negro servant. The old man had worked for the priest's family ever since the priest was a little boy, and he was rather inclined to treat his master like a little boy still, in spite of the fact that he was now almost middle-aged and a man of substance and importance in the village. If the good priest came in wet through, having been caught in the rain while visiting some out-of-the-way cottage in his parish, the old negro would scold and fuss round him like an old hen, or if he was called out late to comfort someone who was ill or dying, the old man would grumble and say that it was not good for him to go out at night and that he ought to wait till morning. Naturally the priest ignored his servant's somewhat maddening ways, for he was not only a man who was tolerant towards everyone, but he was also very fond of the fussy old negro whom he knew regarded him with a deep, protective affection.

One day the priest ordered chicken for dinner and the negro killed a hen from the poultry-yard and made a delicious dish with it. When he had cooked it the smell was so appetizing and good that the old man, being hungry, cut off a leg and ate it and then arranged the dish rather cunningly so that the bird looked quite whole before taking it to his master's table. The priest soon discovered that there was a leg missing and said to his servant, 'Have you eaten a leg off this chicken?'

'No, sir!' said the old negro in shocked tones, shaking his woolly head hard. 'That chicken, sir, he only had one leg when he was alive!'

'Now don't you think I'm fool enough to believe that yarn,' said the priest good-humouredly. 'Come on, you've got a guilty look that gives you away, you know!'

'But holy father, sir, there's any number of hens going around your hen-yard with only one leg,' protested the old man, 'and if you don't believe me, I'll come right in and shout for you the very next time that I notice one!' he added triumphantly.

'All right,' said the priest, looking him fair and square in the eye. 'You do so.'

When the negro happened to see one of the hens standing on one leg he hurried to his master, who was enjoying an after-dinner nap in his chair, and shouted close to his ear. 'Master! Master! Come and see! There's one of the hens, just like I said, what's only got one leg, poor thing!'

So the priest started up and followed his servant out to the hen yard and saw one of the birds standing on one leg, with the other drawn up under its wing. He gave the negro a withering look and said, 'Chuck, chuck, chuckie!' as if he was calling the hens to food and at once the bird put its leg down and ran to him expectantly.

'There! You old rascal!' stormed the priest, 'do you take me for a donkey that you think you can cheat me with your stories of one-legged chickens?'

'No sir, father dear, I'm no cheat. But when you

carved that chicken on your table, you never said
"Chuck, chuck, chuckie" and so you never did find its
other leg!'

The priest gave the negro's hard head a rap and asked
God to forgive him for a liar.

EIGHTEEN

The Boy who was Never Afraid

THERE WAS ONCE a young man who was so brave and fearless that nothing at all could make him afraid. Even as a baby he was never scared or startled by anything and a wise-woman had told his parents that when he grew up he would roam the world having all sorts of adventures, until he came across something that would frighten him. When that happened, the spell that was on him would be broken and he would forget his restless, roving ways and settle down at home.

Normal boys get up to enough mischief, but this boy was an even greater worry to his parents than most. Throughout his childhood he was always mixed up in every prank and escapade that had anything risky or dangerous about it. Long before he was a man he asked his father to give him part of the money he would get when he was grown up so that he could travel far afield in search of more dangerous and difficult feats of adventure.

Reluctantly the father agreed, because he realized that while his boy was under the spell he would never settle down and that he must obey his restless spirit and follow it wherever it drove him.

So the boy said good-bye to his anxious parents and set out with his horse and his servant.

In a short time the youth had become quite famous for his fearless courage, and wherever he went he performed feats of bravery that no one had dared before.

At last he came to a town where he decided to spend the night. All the rooms and inns in the town were full and just as dusk was falling he was told that there was an empty house on the fringe of the town, but that no one dared to enter it as it was supposed to be haunted by a terrible demon. The rich owners of the house had left long ago and now no one ever went there. The young man was quite undaunted by this story and asked where he could find the owner of this haunted house. He was directed to her, for the owner was a lady, and asked if she would allow him to spend the night in her empty house. She gladly agreed, and said he could stay in it for as long as he liked, for she had been unable to find anyone to occupy it for even a single day.

So the young man and his servant settled in to the house for the night. He was quite unafraid of the fact that it was grim and gloomy and that darkness had now fallen. He went to bed and fell asleep as quickly and easily as if he had been in the most comfortable inn in the town.

In the middle of the night, when all was still and silent, the young man was awakened by a strange noise. He listened, quite calmly, and heard a voice ask, 'What would you do if I fell through the ceiling?'

'I shouldn't do a thing,' replied the youth cheerfully. 'You can fall *on* me, if you've a mind to!'

'How shall I come – in one piece, or in many pieces?' asked the ghostly voice.

'You can come in a thousand pieces for all I care,' said the young man.

At that a leg fell into the room with a clatter, this

was followed by an arm, then another leg, then a head and so on until all the parts of a man lay about the youth on the floor. He was not afraid or disgusted, but said quietly and firmly, 'In God's name I command you to stand before me as a whole man and tell me for what reason you haunt this house and try to scare people out of their wits.'

Slowly all the parts of the man merged and melted together until a grim and ghostly figure stood before the youth. It said, in a voice cracked with weariness and sorrow: 'I am the late owner of this house and I have a terrible deed upon my conscience that will not let me rest. When I was alive I took another man's farm and his possessions without any lawful right to them. I am nothing but a thief, a mean, sneaking thief. The only thing that can save my accursed soul is if my wife returns the property to its rightful owner. If you will go to her and tell her what she must do, then I shall be saved and we will all go to heaven.'

The boy replied that he would at once go to the man's widow and tell her his story, so that she could make amends for his wrong-doing. The man thanked the youth and said he had one more thing to ask: 'When you go to my wife,' he said, 'tell her that she must go down to the cellar, where, buried near the largest wine vat, she will find an earthenware pot full of money. But, before you go, bring me an olive branch so that I may place it over the exact spot where the money is buried.'

The young man went outside into the garden and broke off a branch from an olive tree that was growing there. The ghostly man took it from him and laid it over the hidden treasure and then he just melted out of sight. The youth rubbed his eyes and almost could not believe

A ghostly figure stood before the youth.

what he had seen, except that the olive branch still lay where the man had placed it.

It was now nearly morning and the young man made his way to the owner's house to tell her of the night's strange happenings. When she heard him at the door so early she at once supposed that he was scared to stay in the haunted house any longer, but he greeted her calmly and politely and then related his night's adventures. The lady was very upset to hear of the reason for the haunting of her house, and of her dead husband's torment, and said that she would indeed return the farm to its rightful owners, and as quickly as possible, for she knew that they were very poor and homeless. She thanked the youth for his bravery, which would be the salvation of her husband and her family, and they went together to the empty house and down into the cellar, where they found the crock full of money buried beneath the olive branch, just where the ghost had laid it.

The good lady was so grateful to the brave young man that she begged him to stay with them and take her only daughter for his bride. But although the girl was pretty and sweet he had to refuse the mother's offer. 'You do me a great honour, madam,' he said. 'But I am destined to roam the world in search of adventure and for this purpose I must remain a bachelor, with no ties or attachments to bind me.'

The girl said to her mother, 'At least let us give this good gentleman a present of my two favourite doves. I will put them in a basket that he may carry them with him and perhaps their soft voices will remind him of us.'

The youth gladly accepted her gift and, after saying good-bye, set out once more on his travels, in search of further brave deeds to perform.

After they had journeyed many miles and had

stopped for a while to rest in the shade, the servant said to his master: 'Why do you not open the basket? Those poor things do nothing but flutter and are trying to get out.'

So the young man took the basket and pulled out the little peg that fastened the catch. Out burst the two doves, overjoyed to be set free, and they clapped their wings in front of the young man's nose, before circling and soaring away. The young man was so startled by this unexpected noise coming from the gentle doves that he jumped and gave a shudder. For a short second he was afraid – for the first time in his life. And from that moment the spell of restlessness left him and he no longer felt the driving urge to roam and wander. He returned to the widow and thanked her for the lucky gift that had lifted the enchantment from him. He asked for her daughter's hand in marriage, which she granted gladly. After a grand wedding, to which the whole neighbourhood was invited, he returned home to his parents, who were overjoyed to welcome him and his sweet little wife. When they heard that the spell was broken and that he was going to settle down with them for ever, their happiness was complete and the family lived in great joy and contentment and loved each other dearly.

NINETEEN

The King and the Barber

ONCE THERE WAS a nobleman who had three sons. This nobleman was a great friend of the king and the king was very fond of the three boys; in fact, he was god-father to the eldest of them. When the three lads were more or less grown up, the king took them into his service. He appointed the eldest his page, the second his butler and the youngest his barber.

Now the king had only one child, a daughter, and she was the apple of his eye. Few people, he felt, would be good enough to be her husband, and he planned that she should marry some rich and powerful prince, or even a king. But the princess and the king's young barber fell in love with each other. They were so fond of each other that it was obvious to everyone and so it was not long before someone told the king. He was furious and told his daughter that she could not possibly marry the youngest son of a nobleman, who, however good and fine he was, was neither rich nor powerful. She must either promise to give up all idea of marrying him, or he would dismiss him from court and send him miles away.

The princess, who had thought that her father loved her so much that he would let her marry whom she wanted, was very sad when she heard this. She could

K

not decide what to do, so she asked her father for a day in which to think things over, and to this he agreed.

The princess then went to her apartments, and after thinking and thinking she finally made a bundle of her finest clothes and jewels, and with this left the palace by a secret door.

For seven days and nights the princess walked through the forest. She lost her way and must often have gone round in circles, because she did not get so very far. She had only berries and wild fruit to eat and water from the forest streams to drink. There were lots of different kinds of mushrooms in the forest, but the poor girl was not sure which could be eaten and which were poisonous, so she did not dare touch any of them.

Meanwhile, the king was angry and frightened. The palace and its grounds were searched several times over. Everyone in the city and surrounding countryside was asked if they had seen the princess, but nobody had. The poor king was distraught, especially as he knew in his heart of hearts that it was all his fault.

At the end of his seventh sleepless night of worry and anxiety, the king told his young barber that he must go and find the princess, and if he did not bring her back within the year, the king would have him put to death. The young barber, who was just as worried and anxious to find the princess as the king, set out at once.

That evening the princess, who was now feeling very tired and weak from not having enough to eat, heard wolves in the distance. Seeing an enormous oak tree, she put down her bundle and just managed to climb up into the tree. To her surprise, she found that the old tree was hollow, so she stepped down into the big hole, which was quite warm and comfortable, and where she knew no wolf could get her.

She fell asleep, but was woken up a short while later by the noises of someone tethering a horse and settling himself for the night in the shelter of the same big tree. The someone was muttering to himself, and then the princess heard a voice she knew say, 'Oh, I shall never find the princess. What awful luck that with all those pretty girls at court, I should fall in love with the princess. Oh, dear, I love her so, but where can she be.'

Then the princess said:

'Pity the king's daughter, who had to fall in love with her father's barber.'

The hollow oak made the girl's voice sound quite different. In fact, the young man thought he had only been imagining things, and lying down he quickly fell asleep, for he was tired. As soon as his regular breathing told the princess that he was sound asleep she climbed out of her hiding place and dropped to the ground. There she untethered the horse and rode off, taking with her the young man's bundle, which was tied to the pommel, but first changing into his clothes, which he had taken off and were draped over the saddle.

Late that morning the princess reached the kingdom of Leon, and going to the palace there, she offered her services as royal barber. The king of Leon's own barber was an old man whose hand was beginning to shake and the king had long been wanting an excuse to retire him, so he engaged this handsome young man, who seemed so refined and aristocratic, and assigned him apartments in the palace.

When the real barber awoke, the first thing he saw was that his horse was gone. He was angry and frightened, for without a horse how was he going to find his beloved? Then he saw the bundle lying at the foot of the oak. He opened it and was surprised and delighted

. . . quickly fell asleep.

to find the princess's dresses, which meant that she could not be really far away. But then he realized that his own clothes had been taken with the horse. Who, he wondered, could have gone off with it. However, he could not stay as he was in the forest, or anywhere else, so he put on one of the princess's dresses. They were about the same height, and the barber being slim and not very broad-shouldered the dress fitted him quite well. In fact, not having a beard or moustache and his skin being youthfully pink and smooth and his hair long, as was the fashion in those days, the young barber made a very good-looking girl. So, shouldering the princess's bundle and hitching up the skirt of his dress, he strode off following the tracks of his horse.

The trail led him to the palace of the king of Leon. His feet were blistered, his legs ached and he was tired and hungry. The only thing he could think of doing was to pretend that he was the princess, whose dress he was wearing, and he told the page that he was the daughter of the king of Blira and craved audience of the king of Leon. He was quickly ushered in and told the king an imaginary tale of having been separated from the others during a hunt and then having been unseated and the horse taking fright and galloping off. The king was enraptured with the princess, whom he thought the prettiest and nicest girl he had ever met. He made the new princess sit beside him at dinner, and talked with her all the evening. By bedtime he was head over heels in love with the new arrival.

All night the king could not sleep, so very early he sent for his barber so that he could be up and ready to receive the new princess as soon as she awoke. As the real princess was shaving him, the king told her about the new arrival and how he had fallen in love with her.

The princess was delighted to hear that her beloved had managed to follow her, and, as soon as she had finished shaving the king, she hurried to the new princess's room. She found the real barber sound asleep; so, slipping off the barber's clothes, the princess put on her own and picking up her bundle hid in a big cupboard in the room.

When the barber awoke, he was very puzzled to find his own clothes back again and the princess's gone; but there was no help for it, he must just put on what clothes he had. So, a man once more, he left the room in search of breakfast, wondering what story he would tell the king.

The king had been shaved so early that by the middle of the morning he felt that he must be shaved again, before he could meet the princess, so he sent for his barber. There was no one in the barber's room and, no one having seen him, the king decided to do without, and sent a message to the princess that he would be glad to see her. The page knocked on the door, and repeated the message. The real princess, who was inside, was ready and came at once; but when the king saw her he could not believe his eyes. 'Who are you?' he demanded.

'The daughter of the king of Blira, as I told your Majesty yesterday.'

'But it wasn't you!' exclaimed the unhappy king. 'You are my barber. Why are you masquerading in those clothes, and where is the princess I saw yesterday?'

Then the real princess told him the whole story, begging the king's pardon for the deceit she had practised on him, and for making her lover, the barber, deceive him too. Then the real barber came in and told the king that he was the youngest son of the Marquess of Villa Velha, barber to the king of Blira and affianced to his daughter.

The king of Leon was a kindly man with a good sense of humour.

'Well,' he said, 'I have been shaved by the king of Blira's daughter and have made love to his barber. It's high time you two stopped playing tricks on your elders and betters. I shall see that you are well and truly married and that as soon as possible; but till then will you please promise to be yourselves and not mystify me any more.'

They were only too glad to promise this. After the wedding, the king of Leon went with them back to Blira and persuaded the princess's father to forgive her and accept his son-in-law. And the king of Blira had been so frightened, when his daughter ran away, and was so happy to see her safe and well, that he was only too glad to have the young barber, of whom he was very fond, as his son-in-law.

TWENTY

The Count of Estremadura

MANY YEARS AGO there was a king in Portugal who had a beautiful daughter. When she was eighteen he arranged for her to be married to the Count of Estremadura, a wealthy and powerful nobleman from a neighbouring province. As the king was very fond of his daughter he wanted her to meet her future husband, before they were properly engaged, to make sure that she liked him and approved of his choice. So the count was invited to the court, and he duly arrived with a large retinue, for he was very rich indeed. A great banquet was held in his honour, at which the count and princess sat next to each other. The princess seemed very happy and much taken with the handsome count, whereas he was obviously enchanted with the princess's beauty and grace. The old king felt very pleased with himself and was just discussing the ceremonies and celebrations he proposed to hold for the forthcoming marriage, when the count helped himself to a pomegranate that was handed to him from a great piled-up bowl of fruit. As he was eating the pomegranate a seed fell out and dropped on to his beard. He noticed this and picked it off with his fork and popped it into his mouth.

The princess, who had been watching the count all the evening with admiring, though critical eyes, was a fastidious little person and she thought this a most unseemly thing to do; in fact she was quite disgusted by such dreadful behaviour and said in front of everyone at the table that she couldn't possibly marry a man with such dreadful manners. He should have wiped his beard with a napkin, not picked off the seed with his fork. The count was surprised and hurt by the princess's angry tone of voice. He rose from the table and said that he thought it extraordinary that she could refuse to marry him for such an imaginary fault, or attach such importance to trifles. And how could she deliberately shame him in front of all the other guests! Fastidious though she might be the day would come, he said, when she would be glad to eat a crust of dry bread, drink from a dirty ditch and take her meals off straw. The princess flushed and tossed her pretty head scornfully and then the count called for his attendants to follow him and left the king's court. The king was very upset at the way his plans had all gone wrong and felt that his daughter should have been a little more tolerant towards the count who was undoubtedly a very good match and, he thought, a charming fellow.

A short while after this a negro came to the palace and offered himself as a gardener. He was engaged and was often working in the garden when the princess went for her morning walk. The negro gardener had the most beautiful manners; he used to bow respectfully whenever she passed by and he began to make her little nosegays which he would offer to her with a most humble and touching grace. The princess was pleased with his obvious devotion and in a little while they used to talk together whenever the princess walked where the negro was working, which was often, unless it was that the negro was often working where the princess used to walk. Before long the princess discovered that she had fallen in love with the negro gardener and he with her, and they agreed to run away secretly together, for they dare not let the king know of this state of affairs.

Of course, the negro had no horse or carriage, so the little princess had to walk. All the first day they trudged along happily together, keeping to small paths and byways, for they were afraid of being pursued and discovered and there was nowhere they could stop for rest or refreshment. Towards the end of the day the princess was tired out and very hungry and she begged the negro to stop so that she could rest, while he found some food for them both. He said they were miles from any house or inn, but there was a pilgrim coming along the path and perhaps if she asked him he would take pity on her and spare her a crust of bread. This she did, and the pilgrim gave her a piece of dry bread from his bag and she took it gratefully. As she was eating the crust she remembered the count's prophesy: 'You will be glad to eat a crust of dry bread,' and she said, 'Oh count, your words were indeed true.' 'Then,' said the negro, 'will you tell me why you did not love him and marry him, when you had the chance?'

The princess shook her head and they continued on their journey until she was so tired and thirsty that she could not go another step. She begged the negro to try and find a spring that they could drink from, but he looked at her strangely and pointed to a ditch by the roadside saying she would have to drink from the ditch if she was so thirsty, as there was no sign of any other water near. Humbly, the princess knelt down beside the muddy ditch and drank the cloudy water, for she was really parched. Then she again thought of the count's prophetic words and said aloud, 'Oh, count, you spoke

truly when you said I should drink from a dirty ditch.'
The negro said, 'As you would not marry him, perhaps
we should journey to his palace and see if we can seek
work among his many servants, for we cannot travel on
like this with no means of earning a living.'

The princess was too tired and discouraged to think
of any other plan so they journeyed on to the count's
palace, where they were told that there was work for
them to do and that they could shelter in a stable loft
for the night. The poor little princess was so exhausted
that she was thankful for even such a lowly shelter as
this, and sank down upon the straw and asked the negro
if he would beg a little food from the kitchens. He was
gone a long while and when he returned he said he had
had great difficulty in persuading the cooks to spare him
any food and that as he had nothing to carry it in they
had at first refused to give him any, but he had persuaded them to lend him a bowl if he promised to return
it at once and he must tip the food out on to some clean
straw and hurry back with the bowl. The princess asked
how she could possibly eat it, as they had no spoon or
fork, but the negro replied, rather curtly: 'If you're
really hungry, you can eat it with your fingers,' and with
that he hurried away, leaving the princess alone, a truly
humbled little person. She did eat with her fingers, for
she had had nothing all day except the pilgrim's dry
crust of bread, and she once more remembered the
count's prophesy and she cried herself to sleep, thinking
of how differently she would be living now, if she had
stayed behind in her father's palace and married the
count instead of running away with the negro gardener.

The next morning the negro woke her up early and
told her that they must start to do some work for their
living. He had arranged for her to knead the dough in

the palace's bakehouse and he told her that her wage would be so small that she had better steal some of the flour so they could eke out their miserable existence. The princess had never done a stroke of work in her life before, and she was soon hot and tired from kneading the great basins of dough with her delicate hands and her slim little arms ached terribly. Before she finished her work she managed to hide a little bag of flour in her petticoat, although she hated stealing even in her present desperate circumstances, but she was afraid the negro would be angry with her if she disobeyed his instructions.

As she was wearily returning to her shelter in the loft she met the Count of Estremadura, who was looking most handsome and dashing in his fashionable clothes. She passed him with her eyes cast down, but he stopped her and said it had just been reported to him that some flour was missing from his bakehouse and, as she was a new servant, she was suspected of the theft and must be searched. The princess was terrified and when the housekeeper was sent to search her, and found the flour, she was deeply ashamed. The count forbade her to be allowed inside his palace again, but seeing her distress and discomfiture he agreed to let her stay in the loft as she had nowhere else to go.

The little princess then realized that it was the count she really loved and she was stricken with remorse to see him so handsome and desirable and to realize that he was prepared to treat her leniently though she had been caught stealing.

The day after this incident the negro came with the news that the count was soon to be married to a beautiful princess. He said the palace was seething with preparations for the wedding and they were seeking the finest needlewomen to embroider the gorgeous wedding clothes that the bride would wear. As about the only thing the little princess had ever been taught to do with her hands was the most exquisite embroidery, the negro told her that he had arranged that she should be allowed to embroider the wedding dress and that she would receive very good wages for doing it. The princess hid her real feelings from the negro, but when he was gone she burst into tears to think that the count was going to marry another princess and that she herself was now only playing the part of a seamstress when she could have been his bride.

However, she embroidered the dress most skilfully and beautifully, though she often had to wipe away her tears and choke back the lump that came in her throat whenever she thought of the other princess who was going to wear it.

When she had finished and was crying as if her heart would break, the negro came with a number of ladies-in-waiting and pages carrying fine linen, towels and basins of warm, scented water. He said she must hurry to let the ladies help her wash and get dressed in the embroidered wedding gown, as the count's fiancée had not yet arrived and his mother was anxious to see how the gown would look when worn, and had chosen the little princess to try it on as she was exactly the same size as the bride-to-be.

He retired, and the ladies-in-waiting helped the little princess to take off her crumpled travel-stained dress. Then she washed in the lovely rose-scented water and they slipped the glorious rustling silk clothes over her head. First a chemise of finest lawn, then several layers of frothy petticoats and finally the richly embroidered gown itself. They brushed her smooth, dark hair until it shone and the little princess was an exquisite picture of beauty and grace. When she was ready she was taken, not to the count's mother, but to the count himself. He was wearing the most wonderful clothes and jewels and was handsome enough to steal any girl's heart.

Then he told the princess that he was the negro and had disguised himself and gone to her father's palace as a gardener, so that he could be near her without her knowing it. When he had left her father's palace in disgrace he had been so miserable that he realized he was hopelessly in love with the princess and could not possibly live without her. All that he had done was for her own good, so that she could learn some true values.

The princess humbly knelt at his feet, and with her eyes full of tears she kissed his hand and told him that she, too, had realized that the count was her true love and that she had learned to regret her unkind criticism and haughty words. He raised her to her feet and putting his arms round her slender waist he drew her to him and kissed her, saying that all their past differences were now forgotten and that they should be married without delay. They were both dressed in their wedding clothes already and the count had been making all the preparations for his wedding to the princess, although she, of course, had thought it was another girl he was marrying. So they proceeded to the church, in a procession of nobles and pages, and there found everything ready for the ceremony.

The crowds cheered the smiling count and his bride, who had learned wisdom through her difficulties. They loved each other dearly and lived happily ever after.

He was wearing the most wonderful clothes.

TWENTY-ONE

The River

THIS STORY BEGINS at a lonely place in the mountains that now marks the boundary between Portugal and Spain. Into this came an old man and a young girl, his daughter. They walked slowly, as though they had been walking for a long time, as indeed they had, for it was now late in the afternoon and they had left home early that morning and in a great hurry.

The reason for their leaving home was that the girl's father believed he had acquired the enmity of the Enchanted Moors and was afraid that they were going to come and attack him and perhaps carry off his daughter, Joanna. The previous night, unable to sleep, the old man had looked out of his bedroom window and there in his garden by the light of the moon he had seen vague shapes moving about among the trees. What were they? Real or ghosts? The old man was brave, and without hesitation he flung a cloak round his shoulders and, picking up his sword, unlocked a side door that led from his study directly into the garden. Striding out into the moonlight, the old man searched his garden, but in vain, there was no one there. The garden was surrounded by a high wall and he made sure that the two gates in the wall were securely locked, before he went back inside, convinced that the shapes he had seen were Enchanted Moors.

Back in his own room, fears for his daughter's safety overcame him, and, rousing the household, he made all necessary arrangements to shut up the house. He paid and dismissed the servants and took the iron-bound casket in which he kept his gold to a secret place, where he hid it safely.

Then refusing to allow anyone, even old Carlo who had served him with devoted faithfulness for thirty years, to accompany them, he and his daughter set out on foot, having first sewn pieces of leather arranged in a cross on their shoes, for Enchanted Moors can hear the sound of shod hooves, but not of Christian leather. Nonetheless, the old man was in a great hurry to be gone, and he urged his daughter forward.

All day they had walked and now, in the late afternoon, the old man was exhausted. They had just come through the mountains and emerged into this glen, when he announced that he could go no farther and sat down beside a large boulder. The girl, however, was very thirsty and said she must have a look round and see if she could find a stream. The old man was almost afraid to let her out of his sight, but the girl was so thirsty that she insisted that she could not sit down and rest till she had quenched her thirst, so he had to agree, but told her to be most careful and to call out and run back if she saw or heard anything peculiar.

The young girl promised to do this and walked off, searching among the stones and boulders for signs of water. Then at last she heard a rippling, purling sound that could only come from one thing, running water, and a few steps farther on she came across a stream, or rather a mountain torrent. Its bed was narrow and studded with stones round which the water gurgled and chuckled in a lively, bustling way. With a little cry of delight the girl hurried forward and dropped to her knees beside a stone, larger than the rest, in the shelter of which was a pool of calm water. Bending over, the girl was about to plunge her hands in to scoop up some water when she restrained herself, for there, in the water, she could see not her own familiar reflection, but the smiling face of a handsome youth with fair hair and red lips. For an instant their eyes met, then an eddy ruffled the surface of the water. When it had passed, the girl's own face was all that she could see, staring up at her out of the water, lips parted, eyes wide and incredulous. She gazed and gazed; there was nothing to be seen, but her own raven locks and puzzled face, and at last she told herself that she had been imagining things and, plunging in her cupped hands, she scooped up water and drank greedily.

When she had quenched her thirst, the girl remained crouched beside the pool, because she was not quite convinced that she had just imagined that face and not really seen it. The water chuckled and gurgled as though it was amused, and then in the distance she could hear her father's voice calling,

'Joanna! Joanna! Where are you?'

'Here, Father. I've found a stream. I shan't be long.'

'All right, but come soon,' called the old man's voice.

Joanna knelt there, gazing at the water then, suddenly, as well as her own reflection, she could see the head and shoulders of a fair-haired, handsome young man, the same face she had seen before.

Convinced that someone was standing over her, looking down, Joanna leaped to her feet and turned to face the stranger; but there was no one there. She scanned the stretch of rough, boulder-strewn ground but there was nothing to be seen, not a sign of anyone or anything. Again she wondered whether she might not be imagining things, but then a laughing voice behind her said,

'Who are you? And where have you come from?'

Joanna spun round, her heart in her mouth, but there was no one there either. She realized now that she could not have been imagining things and began to feel afraid. In a voice that was little more than a whisper, she said,

'Who are you? And where are you?'

'Look down,' said the voice.

Joanna looked down at the stony ground. There was nothing there.

'Not there,' said the voice. 'Here.'

Joanna looked at the pool and there it was again. For an instant she saw the same smiling face as before. Then the sound of her father's voice calling 'Joanna', made her turn her head away and, when she looked back, the face was there no longer. Again her father called and now there was a note of urgency in his voice. Joanna got to her feet and took a hesitant step back.

'Don't go,' said a voice, a voice that to her was the nicest she had ever heard.

'I must,' Joanna said. 'My father is there and getting anxious.'

'Then come back,' said the voice.

'I'll try,' Joanna promised.

'If you don't, I shall follow you,' said the voice.

'Joanna!' the old man shouted.

'Coming,' called Joanna, and turning, she walked back to where her father still sat beside the boulder.

'You've been a long time,' the old man said in a grumbly voice.

'I was so thirsty, Father. I had to drink and drink.'

'Well, now we must sleep,' Joanna's father said. 'It's

almost dark and we're tired. But we must take it in turns, one keeping guard while the other sleeps, just in case the Enchanted Moors have followed us.

'I'm not sleepy,' Joanna said. 'Honestly, I'm not. You sleep first, I'll watch.'

Grumblingly the old man assented. Joanna waited till her father's breathing told her that he was asleep, then getting up as quietly as she could, she tiptoed away.

There was no moon, or rather it was hidden behind clouds, and the night was so dark that Joanna scarcely saw the dark shapes of the boulders in time to prevent herself walking into them. Once or twice her toe struck a stone and sent it scurrying, and her heart went into her mouth and she paused and waited fearfully to see if the sound had woken her father. But he slept on, or at best did not call out, as he would have done, if he had woken properly and discovered her gone; so Joanna walked on again.

Coming to the stream she knelt down beside the pool and whispered, 'Here I am. I've come!' at the same time as her eyes strained to see into the waters of the pool.

'I'm here,' Joanna whispered again and this time her straining eyes seemed to detect a swirl in the dark waters, and the next moment the clouds parted and the moon shone out, and there in the bright waters of the pool was the handsome face of the young man whose voice had so touched her heart.

'I'm glad you've come,' said the voice. 'How lovely you are, the loveliest girl I have ever seen. Tell me, who are you and what are you doing here?'

In an eager whisper Joanna told the story of her father's sudden fears and their hasty departure from the home she loved so dearly. Where they were going she said she had no idea. She did not think that even her father knew. All he wanted was to hurry on so as to get away from his enemies and persecutors.

'Stay here,' said the voice. 'There are trout in this and other pools. You can make a line with your black hair and a hook with your brooch and never be hungry. Stay here so that I can feast my eyes on you and listen to your voice.'

'How can I?' Joanna said. 'My father is impatient to get on, and even if I dared stay here alone he would not allow it. I must go with him and I know that as soon as he wakes he will be impatient to be on his way.'

'Then I shall follow you,' said the voice.

'Oh! Can you come out, then? Are you real? I mean a real person?'

'Alas, I cannot leave the water. But the only way out from this glen, except that by which you have come, is to follow the course of this stream. It will take you two days before you get out from here. Wherever you halt to rest or sleep you must come to me, so that I can see you and hear your dear voice.'

'I will,' whispered Joanna. 'Now I must go back. I'm so afraid my father will wake up, and if he finds me gone he will be wild with anxiety.'

So Joanna got to her feet and hurried back to where her father lay. He stirred as she lay down in her place, but did not awaken. Joanna lay there thinking of the strange thing that had happened to her, her heart filling with sudden happiness and a great yearning for that fair face and glorious voice.

In the morning, when her father woke, he reproved her for not waking him so that he could take his turn at watching, but he was too relieved at being told that she had neither seen nor heard any signs of the Enchanted Moors, to be angry with her.

They ate some of the food they carried in a satchel, and then the old man got to his feet and announced that they must hurry on. Joanna suggested that they follow the stream she had found, for that surely must lead them out of the glen, and her father agreed.

All that day Joanna sang as she walked along. Her face was bright with happiness and her father wondered at the change that had come over her, for the day before she had been sad and almost angry at having to leave home.

And he wondered too at a strange sound that filled the air, a deep rushing sound, but whenever he asked Joanna what it might be, she pretended not to be able to hear it or to know what he was talking about. But she knew that it was *he*, following in the stream as he had said he would, and her heart beat faster. Several times she knelt down by the bank to drink, hoping for a sight of that smiling face and laughing eyes, but he was not visible.

All day they walked. Then when the sun hung low, though evening had not yet fallen, the old man announced that they should stop for that day. In the first place his feet were now blistered and sore, and as there had been no sign of the Enchanted Moors he felt that perhaps they had not got on to their track. So, finding a sheltered spot, they made themselves as comfortable as possible.

As soon as they had eaten the old man settled down to sleep, telling Joanna that she should do the same, for he felt that there was perhaps no need to keep watch that night. Joanna curled up and pretended to be sleepy, but as soon as she could hear that her father was asleep, she got up and quietly walked to the stream. Kneeling down, she called quietly:

'Here I am! Here I am!'

There was no answer, but the rustle of grasses stirring in the wind. Again she called:

'Here I am! Here I am!'

And this time the waters swirled as though in answer, and there was his fair face smiling up at her.

For a long time they talked and then he told her that she and her father had walked so fast that they would be out of the glen by the next afternoon; beyond that he could not go, because there the stream ran into a river into which he must not enter. A great sadness came over them then and Joanna felt that her heart would break.

'If only you could come out!' she said.

'That is impossible,' he answered. 'But you could come to me.'

'But my father,' Joana said, 'what about him?'

'Tomorrow he will reach the open country, where there are many houses and people who can look after him. He will be all right.'

Finally Joanna let herself be persuaded, and getting to her feet she stepped into the water, where cool arms enfolded her and bore her happily down.

* *

When Joanna's father woke and found his daughter vanished, he at first thought she had gone to the stream to wash, but when there was no answer to his calls, he became afraid and desperate. He ran up and down shouting and calling in a frenzy, but there was no answer to his calls and nowhere could he see a sign of his daughter. Convinced that the Enchanted Moors had

... there was his face smiling up at her.

taken her, the sad and unhappy old man set off down-stream towards the places where people lived, and at every cottage to which he came, he knocked at the door and asked if anyone had seen a girl pass that way. But no one had.

And now, if you should go to that stream and listen to its waters, you would hear two voices: one a man's and one a woman's, chattering and laughing and chuckling, and you would know that they were happy.

TWENTY-TWO

The Palace of the White Cat

A LITTLE WAY BACK from the sloping left bank of the River Mira is an eminence on which in the olden days stood a palace. The ground between the gates of the palace and the river bank was covered with olive trees, and a hedge of wild aloes formed a formidable obstacle to any intruder rash enough to wish to gain access to the palace. The strange thing about this palace was that its owner was a white cat. It was all a great mystery, but the palace had been there so long – longer than anyone could remember – that people had ceased to wonder or even to gossip about it. It had been there since long before the Moors had left and that was all that people knew, for though the White Cat's servants were obviously human, they were both deaf and dumb and either could not, or would not, understand signs.

The palace was a magnificent mansion and behind it was a garden beautifully laid out with lots of little lakes round which stood beautifully carved statues of young men and women. The sculptors who had carved them must have had genius, because they looked alive, as though they were just standing stock still, gazing sorrowfully into the water. At night, strings of lanterns and fairy lights were lit round the lakes, and from inside the palace came the sound of music that was lovely, even though sad.

The few who had seen the White Cat said that she was a beautiful creature. Her fur was like velvet and her eyes like pearls. But not many had seen even that much and most people were no longer even curious.

One day interest in the White Cat revived when a knight in armour, mounted on a coal-black horse, rode up to the principal inn of the town which lay a bare half-mile from the White Cat's palace. The knight's shield bore the effigy of a white cat rampant and beneath it the device: 'Invincible'. The knight dismounted and, going inside, ordered a meal. Having eaten, he remounted his big black horse and galloped off in the direction of the White Cat's palace. He did not return. In fact he was never seen again. Some people said that he had gone into the palace and never come out again. Others insisted that he had left the town by the other road, though none had seen him go. Next day the towns-people flocked out to stare through the great gates of the White Cat's palace, where they saw the White Cat walking in the grounds and decided she was looking sadder than ever.

It must have been a month or more later when another knight in full armour rode into the town and inquired the way to the White Cat's palace. This knight was riding a grey horse. His shield bore the same emblem of a white cat rampant beneath which were the words: 'I win or die'. Having inquired where the White Cat's palace lay, the knight rode off in that direction and was seen no more. Again the towns-people went out to see what was to be seen at the palace. All they saw was the White Cat looking sadder than ever.

Four weeks later a third knight came to the town. This time he was a young and handsome youth, but, though his face was young, he bore himself with a quiet dignity that hushed the throng of eager chatterers that had collected at the news of his arrival. This young knight was fully equipped and rode a big bay charger with a lovely arching neck and sweeping tail. He, too, dismounted and, entering the inn, ordered a simple meal. When he had finished, his horse was led out and he mounted and rode off in the direction of the White Cat's palace. People's curiosity had by this time been so aroused that quite a crowd followed him out along the road that led to the river and the White Cat's palace. Thus it was that on this occasion there were witnesses of what actually took place.

The young knight, on whose shield was a plain red cross instead of the white cat rampant, rode up to the palace gates and with one strong thrust of his lance flung them wide open. The clang of the gates was answered by a terrific roar from the palace. The on-lookers saw a sheet of fire burst from the great palace door, out of which emerged a moment later the most horrible dragon you can imagine. It was enormous and its long tail, with which it lashed the air in evident fury, caused such a wind that the trees and bushes bent as if a gale had sprung up.

The young knight seemed unimpressed, or at least undaunted. He sat his horse, lance in hand, surveying the dragon, as though looking for the best place to strike. Suddenly the crowd gave a gasp, as they saw that the dragon held the White Cat in its great talons. A moment the young knight waited, then urging his great bay horse forward he couched his lance and rode full tilt at the dragon.

The knight and his horse were one. The horse never slackened its pace till it felt the jar of the lance going home, then it reared back on its haunches to break its career, the knight slipped from the saddle, drew his sword and cut off the dragon's monstrous head. As the dragon's head touched the ground, ten enormous snakes suddenly appeared and began trying to enfold the knight in their coils; but he was too quick for them, and seizing each in his two mailed hands he strangled them. As each fell, it turned into two black vultures, and soon the young knight had twenty of these great birds attacking him and trying to peck his eyes out. But even though they were twenty, the knight managed to keep them off with his sword and one by one he killed them.

As the last bird fell flapping to the ground, the knight found himself surrounded by forty dark-haired, almond-eyed girls, each one lovelier than the next, who smiled ingratiatingly and seemed to want to throw their arms round him. Unable to believe that they could mean him well, the knight tried to fend them off, then he heard a voice gasp: 'Strike! Strike!' and looking down he saw the White Cat panting. If that was what was needed, then strike he would, and raising his sword he cut off their heads with twenty sweeping blows. As they rolled across the ground, the heads turned into burning coals. The ground seemed covered with red hot coals and the White Cat would undoubtedly have been most horribly burned, probably killed, if the knight had not stooped and scooped her up in his shield. As the White Cat touched the cross that was painted on the shield, inside

... these great birds attacked him.

and out, the very air seemed full of sound; all the statues round the lake came to life and began running towards the knight while the White Cat herself suddenly turned into a beautiful girl dressed in elaborate and magnificent oriental clothes.

As soon as the girl who had been the White Cat had recovered, and the knight got over his surprise, she told him her story.

Her name was Mizpah and she was the only daughter of Mudi Ben Raschid, for many years Moorish governor of that part of the country in the days long ago, when Almandazar the Magnificent was alive. Her mother was the daughter of Alchazar, governor of Mazagan. She was a good wife and a loving mother, and they had all been happy till Mizpah's father had discovered that his wife had forsaken the religion of her people and become a Christian. After that he told her that he would have nothing more to do with her until she returned to the Moslem fold, and she died of a broken heart. The girl's father then married again, but his second wife was a wicked woman. She knew that Mizpah was at heart a Christian too and that she was in love with a Christian. This knowledge she kept to herself till one evening, when there was a great banquet. Then she said to her husband:

'Mudi Ben Raschid, the crescent of the Holy Prophet is waning in your family – your daughter is a renegade!'

When he heard that, Mizpah's father was very, very angry indeed. He banged his fist on the table and said that he would rather lose all his money and possessions, rather have a white cat for a daughter, than have such a stain on the honour of his family. No sooner had he said that and was raising his fist to emphasize it with a further thump, than he fell dead. At that there was a tremendous roar and a great rumbling. Mizaph's step-mother, who was the cause of all the trouble, fell dead too, which served her right. All the courtiers, pages and other guests attending the banquet were turned into stone, as was the young man with whom Mizpah was in love, Haroun, while Mizpah herself was turned into a white cat. The palace servants remained alive, but were struck dumb and deaf.

Since that awful day, long, long before, many a brave knight, hearing of what had happened to the beautiful Mizpah, had tried to save her, but one and all had failed to overcome the great dragon. This was because they had relied only on themselves, while the young knight had put his trust in the cross as well as in his own strong arms, and so he had been able to kill the dragon and thus transform the maiden and bring the others back to life.

'So,' said the girl, as she finished her story, 'I am the prize of your sword and you may deal with me as you will.'

The knight assured her that he considered it both a duty and a pleasure to rescue maidens in distress. The truly chivalrous, he told her, found all the reward they could desire in doing what they considered their duty and in restoring happiness to those who had lost it. He himself had already rescued a number of people in various parts of the world and had other similar tasks awaiting him. He hoped that Mizpah would live long and happily. Then, bowing low, or as low as he could in his armour, he swung himself into the saddle. Saluting, he turned his horse's head and rode out through the golden gates.

As soon as the palace could be put in order and a banquet prepared, Mizpah and her Haroun were married. They invited all the townspeople to their wedding and at the banquet everyone drank the health of the young knight, who, it was whispered, was St. James of Compostella.

TWENTY-THREE

The Beautiful Princess

LONG, LONG AGO there was a prince, the only son of his father, the king, and consequently rather spoiled and conceited, though really a very nice and likeable young man at heart. The time came when the prince decided that he ought to marry, but none of the princesses in the neighbouring kingdoms was to his liking, for he had a high ideal of beauty and of what he owed to himself. So the prince arrayed himself in a coat of mail that was made of such fine links it was as soft and supple as silk, and with a small retinue he set off to look for a bride. He rode through the length and breadth of Europe visiting every capital and attending every banquet or gala performance, where he might see princesses. In his mind's eye he had a picture of the girl he was looking for, a vision of perfect loveliness, which apparently he was never going to find. The prince saw and met lots of pretty princesses, but none of them were like the picture he carried in his mind, and all had some fault of figure or character that made him feel that he did not want to be married to her.

So, sadly he turned away from the court of the king of Muscovy and set off on his way home. But he could not be sad for long, for he was at heart a jolly fellow and loved a laugh. And the prince also had a passion for

With a small retinue he set off.

fairs. If there was one being held anywhere near, as he made his way back across Europe, he would go to it and try his skill at archery and other contests, look at the fat lady and the dancing bears and have his fortune told by gypsies, who all told him different things. Then, one evening, when he was walking round the gay scene of a fairground outside the ancient town of Coblenz, the prince suddenly stopped, for there, on one of the stalls, was the picture of the girl for whom he was looking. It was her exactly! The prince went to the stall in a state of great excitement and asked the man who the girl in the picture was. The man told him that she was the daughter of a certain king in the Far East, and that he had bought the picture from the artist who had painted it, who told him that the king had refused to accept it as he said the artist had not made the princess nearly beautiful enough. So the prince bought the picture and at once set off for home.

When he arrived home he went to his father and showed him the picture, telling him that he would marry this girl or none. The picture showed a face of such beauty, grace and dignity that could only have been produced by noble birth and breeding, and the king was delighted that his son had at last succeeded in his search. It was a pity, of course, that the girl was so far away, but the king had a ship fitted out and sent his chancellor to ask for the girl's hand in marriage.

When the chancellor reached the court of the oriental king whose daughter's portrait the prince had bought at the fair, he explained how the prince had sought a bride all over Europe and never found one beautiful enough, and then had seen the portrait of the oriental king's daughter and fallen in love with her. The king felt very flattered and so did his daughter. Furthermore when she heard all the nice – and true – things the chancellor had to say about the young prince, she agreed to marry him. The chancellor then produced a magnificent ring the prince had given him and set it on the princess's finger.

As soon as matters could be arranged the princess was married to the prince by proxy, and a cabin in the ship was specially fitted out to accommodate her on the long voyage back to Portugal. As soon as this was completed they set sail.

When they came within sight of the coast of Portugal, a messenger was put ashore to ride day and night to take the news to the prince that the chancellor had succeeded in his mission and that the prince was now married to the girl on whom he had set his heart, who would be with him in a few days' time. There were great rejoicings at the news and feverish preparations went on to welcome the princess. Arrangements were made for a great display of horsemanship, together with races, for this was one of the prince's favourite sports. A luxurious pavilion was built to which the princess was to be conducted on her arrival and from which she could witness the contests.

The prince felt he must see his bride before he went to meet her officially, just to satisfy himself that she was the same girl as in the portrait he had bought, so, leaving his father to welcome the princess, he put on a disguise and mingled with the crowd outside the pavilion. He watched the procession arrive and then saw a number of women enter the pavilion. Going up to the rails the prince inquired of one of the pages who had accompanied the princess, which was she, and the page, for a joke, pointed to one of the princess's maids-of-honour who was dreadfully plain and said, 'That's the princess.'

The prince's heart sank. For a moment he felt that he wanted to cry, but then he became icily angry, feeling convinced that the old fool of a chancellor had let himself be tricked. However, there was nothing the prince could do, because he was already married, but he decided that he would never look at that face again. He sent a message to his father and the princess saying that he was unavoidably detained and begged them to excuse him, as he could not get back till late.

The king entertained the princess and saw her installed in her new home. She was quite mystified by the prince's behaviour, as was his father. The banquet of welcome was held with the prince's chair empty, and the princess was in bed before the prince returned. From then on he refused to have any lights in their apartments and every morning arose before dawn and rode off to his estates to supervise the work of the farms. The poor princess was mystified, mortified and very unhappy. So it went on for days and weeks. Then, one day, when the princess was walking alone in the palace grounds, an old woman came up to her and said:

'The secrets of many hearts are revealed to me. I know why you are unhappy and I know a way to cure your unhappiness, but you must do what I tell you.'

'I will do anything,' said the princess. 'Anything rather than endure this unhappiness.'

'Then go and borrow some plain, simple clothes, put them on and come back to me here.'

The princess did this, and when she rejoined the old woman they set off together for the prince's country estate. On reaching it the old woman asked the bailiff if she might take 'her daughter' for a walk across the fields as she had been ill and the doctor had recommended her to take country air. She was given permission and before long they came – as the woman had intended – to where the prince was watching some men shearing his sheep. He could scarcely believe his eyes when he saw the girl of his dreams wearing a plain, homely dress and walking along beside the old woman. Before he had time to recover his wits and decide what to do, the princess and the old woman had walked on and were out of sight.

That night the prince was very silent and seemed preoccupied, and all the next morning he could do nothing but wonder who the girl was whom he had seen walking the day before. That afternoon, hearing footsteps while standing outside a farmhouse he used as a week-end cottage, he looked up and saw the girl again. This time she was walking by herself and the prince stood still and waited for her to come up. To his delight the girl stopped and in a quiet little voice asked if he could possibly let her have a drink of water. The prince was delighted to do anything for the girl, and going inside he brought back a drink in a jewelled silver goblet. The girl thanked him and drank, then carelessly she let the goblet fall on to the stones, on which it smashed and a splinter flying from it cut her foot. It was not a deep or bad cut, and the girl refused the prince's help and just tied her hanky round it and walked on, telling the prince, who had said how much he would like to see her again, that she was sure they would meet soon.

That night the prince was wakened by his wife, who told him that her foot was hurting and asked him to look at it. The prince said that he would send the doctor in the morning; but his young wife insisted that he look then and there, because it was hurting very much. So, very reluctantly, the prince struck a light and was surprised to see that his wife's foot was cut in the same place as the girl's had been. Then, at last, the stubborn prince did what he should have done long before and looked at his wife's face and saw that she was indeed the lovely girl of his dreams and the one to whom he had given a drink that afternoon.

The prince was very contrite for having been so stupid, but his wife being a kind-hearted girl and in love with her husband was only too glad to forgive him, and after that there was no happier couple in all Portugal than the prince and his bride from the East.

The prince ordered that the page who had played such a nasty trick on him and caused them both so much unhappiness, be given a good whipping, and I, personally, think he richly deserved it.

TWENTY-FOUR

The Blind King and the Magic Bird

WHEN A SON was born to the king and queen of a certain province in Portugal, they invited all the astrologers and magicians in the land to come and cast his horoscope, which means they would tell his fortune and forecast what his future would be. The king and queen looked forward to a bright and prosperous future for their baby son, so you can imagine the burden of grief which fell on them when these wise-men all foretold exactly the same thing: that the prince would be a misfortune to his father and would be the cause of his death by means of a dagger.

The king was so upset that he secretly decided to get rid of the baby boy. In his apartments he had a chest, and this he now had lined with satin and velvet. Then, one night, he stealthily lifted the sleeping baby from its cradle, laid it gently in the chest and carried it down to the courtyard, where he had ordered his horse to be ready waiting. Mounting, he put the chest in front of him and rode off into the night. A few miles from the palace he came to a river and there he dismounted and threw the chest far out into the stream. He watched while it was swept away and then, with mixed feelings, rode back to the palace.

In the morning there was a dreadful commotion when the loss of the baby was discovered. The queen wept and would not be comforted and insisted that the king should send out search parties to look for the baby, but no trace of him was ever found and after several years the poor queen had given up all hope of ever seeing her son again.

When the king threw the chest into the river, it had been carried downstream for several miles until the current swept past a mill. Here the chest had come to rest against the mill-wheel. The miller and his wife heard a baby crying and, hurrying out, they had traced the cries to the chest which they could see lodged against the wheel. Carefully they pulled the rich-looking chest from the water and opened the lid and there, lying on the quilted satin lining, was a darling little baby boy. He was so perfectly made, so beautiful and adorable, even though his little face was puckered and purple with rage, that the miller and his wife were quite breathless with excitement and happiness, for they had no child of their own and were convinced that the fairies had at last granted their dearest wish and sent them this child.

The miller's wife looked after the baby with care and devotion and throughout his childhood he was a joy to his parents. When he had grown to be a lad and old enough to learn a trade, they asked him what he wanted to be when he grew up and he replied, 'A tailor'. So they apprenticed him to the best tailor in the district, where he proved to be the cleverest of pupils. When he had served his apprenticeship he set up on his own and before long he became famous for the beauty and skill of his workmanship.

When he was known as the best master tailor in the neighbourhood, news of his fame had spread even to the palace. When the queen heard of him, she sent for him and thought she would try his skill by ordering a dress for her Moorish slave, a girl of noble birth, but who was a slave because she had been captured in the wars against the Moors. The tailor came to the palace and was shown to the queen's apartments. She ordered him to make a dress for her slave-girl and he bowed low and said the finished dress would be delivered by the following morning. The queen was amazed that he left without taking any measurements, but she was even more amazed when the next morning the dress was delivered, not only most beautifully made, but also a perfect fit. The queen was, of course, delighted and sent for the tailor again, this time to order a dress for herself. She told him what material she wanted for the dress, and how she would like it shaped and embroidered and promised him a rich reward if he would have it ready by the following day. Again the tailor left without taking any measurements and again the dress was delivered punctually the next morning, exactly as the queen had ordered and fitting her like a glove.

The queen wanted to pay handsomely for the two dresses, but the tailor absolutely refused to accept any money, saying that it was an honour for him to be allowed to present them to the queen. So, instead of money, she asked him if he would accept a gift from her. 'Gladly,' replied the tailor, and the queen opened a chest in which she kept all sorts of valuables. There were jewels and gold and silver ornaments, ivory carvings and all sorts of precious things. The tailor chose a beautiful dagger from the collection: the back of the blade was finely engraved and the handle was made of ivory, set with rubies and diamonds. He thanked the queen for her beautiful gift and was leaving her apartments when the king entered. Seeing a stranger coming from the queen's private apartments he flew into a jealous rage and drew his sword to strike the stranger. The tailor tried to defend himself with his new dagger but the king, now thoroughly roused at seeing the other's weapon, which he knew belonged to the queen, rushed furiously at him and would have killed the tailor if he had not first stabbed the king. The king fell to the ground, wounded, and the queen came hurrying in with some of her attendants to see what the commotion was about. When she saw the king lying on the ground, with blood flowing from a stab-wound and the tailor standing with the dagger in his hand, she shrieked for her pages to seize him and ordered them to strip him and flog him.

They tore the tailor's shirt from his back and started to thrash him when the queen suddenly cried out to them to stop! She had seen on the tailor's back a birthmark exactly the same as the one on the back of her long-lost son. She was in a state of great confusion, not knowing what to believe or even what she wanted to believe. The king was seriously wounded and she wanted vengeance for his attacker, yet hope had risen in her, the hope she had long ago abandoned, of seeing her own son again.

She sent messengers out to search the district and make inquiries about the tailor and his home and parents, while she kept him a prisoner at the palace, and after several days the messengers returned with the miller, who was brought before the wounded king and the queen to be questioned. He told them how he and his wife had found their son when he was a baby floating in the river in a chest, which had drifted against their mill-wheel. In a weak voice the king asked the miller to describe the chest. 'Your majesty, it was a rich looking chest, covered with velvet and lined with quilted satin,' said the miller. 'Alas, this man is indeed my son,' said the king and turning to his wife he asked her to come close to him. He was so weak that she could scarcely hear what he had to say, but with his last breath he whispered how he had secretly disposed of the baby. He asked her to forgive him – then he died.

The queen sent for her son to be released from his chains, for he was now the true king and must be enthroned with due pomp and ceremony. When he heard that it was his own father that he had killed he was overcome with horror and remorse, but he had no alternative but to undertake the government of his kingdom. However, on the day that he was crowned there was a terrible storm, and as the golden crown was set upon his head a vivid flash of lightning pierced the sky and the young king was blinded by it.

The court physicians were called to examine his eyes, but all their remedies failed to restore his sight. The queen sent for doctors from far away but all their efforts were in vain. At last, in desperation, she decided to consult a witch and for this purpose she set out alone, dressed in a simple hood and cloak, to the witch's cottage which was in the depths of a dark forest. In spite of the queen's plain clothes, the witch greeted her as the queen, for it was said that there were no secrets hidden from her and she had already guessed the purpose of the queen's visit. In a croaky voice she told the queen that the young king's sight could only be restored if his eyes were brushed with a feather from a magic bird which lived on the highest tree in the world in a far-off land. Moreover, the feather must be plucked by a young maiden of noble birth.

The queen returned to the palace and sent for all the maidens of noble birth that she could summon. She ordered them to find the bird and bring back one of its feathers, but although many of them succeeded in finding the huge tree and even of catching a glimpse of the magic bird, none of them could ever get near it to pluck a feather, for it was very timid and flew away at the sight of a human being.

At last the queen's slave girl, the Moorish lady for whom the tailor had once made a dress, asked if she could not be allowed to go in search of the magic bird. She had fallen in love with the young, blind king and would have done anything to cure his blindness. The queen gave her permission to try, although by this time she had very little hope of her son ever being cured.

The slave girl travelled to the distant country, patiently searched for the huge tree and when she reached it she saw the magic bird perched amongst the topmost branches. It was fluttering with its wings and bowing its head up and down as if to beckon her towards it, and the sun shone and flashed on its beautiful metallic feathers. The slave girl started to climb the great tree, and she was so slim and light that she was able to reach the topmost branches and there she gently stretched her hand towards the bird and it shed a gleaming green feather into her hand. Eagerly she tucked the feather into her bodice and swiftly descended from the tree, and then she began the long journey back to the palace of the blind king.

When she arrived, she went to the king and gently stroked his eyelids with the magic feather. His eyes

opened and he looked into the dark, lustrous eyes of the
Moorish slave – and fell in love with her.

There was great rejoicing in the land at the news that
the king was blind no longer, and when he announced
that he was going to marry the Moorish girl who had
given him back his sight, the queen was delighted and
ordered a great banquet and joyful celebrations. The
couple were married with everyone's blessing, and they
had seven beautiful children, all bearing the same
strange little birthmark on their backs as their father.
The happy king and his young queen ruled the country
wisely and well.